THE
ART
OF
BENIN

A Catalogue of an Exhibition of the

A. W. F. FULLER

and

CHICAGO NATURAL HISTORY MUSEUM

Collections of Antiquities from Benin, Nigeria

BY PHILIP J. C. DARK

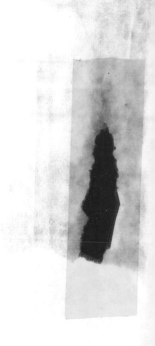

Library of Congress Catalog Card No. 62-20854

© 1962 by Chicago Natural History Museum
Printed in Chicago, Illinois, U.S.A.

CONTENTS

CAPTAIN A. W. F. FULLER

The importance to this exhibition of the Benin specimens from the Fuller Collection focuses attention upon Captain A. W. F. Fuller, whose life-long interest was the assembling of an outstanding collection of ethnological specimens from Africa and the South Seas.

Alfred Walter Francis Fuller was born on March 29, 1882, the second son of the Reverend Alfred Fuller. His family had lived in Sussex for some six hundred years prior to his father's removal to London. After studying engineering at Dulwich College, Captain Fuller undertook the study of law and was admitted as a solicitor of the High Court. His promising career in the legal profession was brought to an abrupt end by the outbreak of World War I, when the future Captain resigned from his legal firm and enlisted in the Army as a private in the Oxford and Buckinghamshire Light Infantry. He specialized in explosives and trench warfare and was soon appointed to the brigade staff as trench warfare officer, later being promoted to the grade of captain. He served on the Salonica front in 1917 and was subsequently appointed trench mortar officer for the Corps. In this capacity he founded and commanded the Corps school. In September he accompanied his regiment on the expedition through the Carpathian Mountains and was in active combat throughout Serbia and Bulgaria. At the end of 1918 he returned to England, broken in health, and was transferred to the Army Reserves for a three-year period, after which he retired in grade of captain with a disability pension.

At a very early age Captain Fuller undertook the hobby of collecting. He recounts that at age four his favorite collected item was a wingless death's-head moth which he carried with him everywhere he went. In his collecting he received the sympathetic interest of his father, who apparently had throughout his life collected natural history specimens of all kinds. From his father, also, he learned to distinguish the fine specimen from the ordinary. After moving to London, the Reverend Fuller found increased opportunities to enrich his collections through attending the auction sales in that city. It was here that young Walter, who invariably accompanied him to sales, became interested in ethnology, his first purchase being a club from the Fiji Islands. From that time on throughout his life he continued adding to his collection the fine and the unusual, as well as careful selections of the typical. In the later years of his life his vast collections from Oceania, Africa, and North America taxed the capacity of his lovely Eng-

1

lish cottage in the Tulse Hill section of southwest London.

The fame of the Fuller Oceanic Collection caused it to be known to all major institutions working in the field of ethnology, as well as to many private collectors. Repeatedly, offers for selected specimens were made to Captain Fuller. Repeatedly, he rejected them, saying that the collection which had been the work of his lifetime was not to be broken up.

A few years ago contact was made with Captain Fuller in the hope of obtaining for Chicago Natural History Museum the entire Oceanic collection. Captain Fuller reacted with little enthusiasm at first, but, as he became more fully informed on the standing and methods of this institution, he became convinced that the Museum should be the depository of his vast and wonderful collection. As all his collected materials had been given to Mrs. Fuller, it was necessary that she concur in his decision, which she readily did.

Captain Fuller knew every one of his specimens intimately and for the most part recalled precisely the circumstances under which each was obtained. So valuable was this store of information that the Museum arranged that his comments regarding each of the Oceanic specimens were to be recorded so that this vast fund of information might not be lost.

Captain Fuller was a rare example of a man who would not permit adversity and ill health to deter him in the pursuit of a worthy lifetime calling. Perhaps his ill health even aided him, in that he was unable to carry on activities in the legal profession for which he had been trained. The assembling of his beloved specimens was an activity which could be undertaken during those times when his health permitted. It was fortunate indeed that Mrs. Fuller, the former Estelle Winifred Cleverly, encouraged him in his ambition and aided him greatly in the care of the collections. A lasting memorial to Captain Fuller, and a major contribution to the study of Oceanic ethnology, was the joining of the outstanding Fuller Oceanic Collection with the comprehensive Oceanic collections of Chicago Natural History Museum.

Captain Fuller in negotiating the sale of the Oceanic collection found to his own surprise that his deep interest in it was transferred to Chicago Natural History Museum. Frequently his letters contained mention of "our Museum," and it was his plan to visit the Museum shortly after the collection had been transferred. Unfortunately, Captain Fuller, who always worked beyond the limits of his failing strength, was never to realize his hope for the visit. It was with deep regret that the Museum learned of his death on December 13, 1961, shortly after he and Mrs. Fuller had arranged to send to the Museum the Benin specimens which are a part of this exhibition.

We are fortunate in being able to exhibit with our own Benin material the Fuller Collection of Benin art, which is one of the major Benin collections existing today.

CLIFFORD C. GREGG, *President*
Chicago Natural History Museum

ACKNOWLEDGMENTS

The generosity of Mrs. A. W. F. Fuller has made possible the exhibition, "The Art of Benin," for fully half of the objects exhibited have been loaned to Chicago Natural History Museum by Mrs. Fuller. The high quality of the Fuller Benin Collection has long been known, but this exhibition is the first occasion on which the major portion of it has been publicly shown. Mrs. Fuller has aided the Museum in many ways, and we are grateful to her for this further expression of her interest.

I should like to thank the City Art Museum of St. Louis and its Director, Dr. Charles Nagel, for the loan of a fine early bronze head and for permission to publish a photograph of it. Dr. Bradbury has also kindly contributed a number of field photographs for the exhibition, and I thank him for their use.

Dr. Philip J. C. Dark, Professor of Anthropology at Southern Illinois University, the author of this catalogue, has served as consultant and, with Phillip Lewis, Curator of Primitive Art of Chicago Natural History Museum, has planned the exhibition. We are greatly indebted to Dr. Dark for his assistance.

The photographs, except the one of the St. Louis head, were made by John Bayalis and Homer V. Holdren, Division of Photography, Chicago Natural History Museum.

The exhibition was designed by Susan Schanck, artist-preparator of the Department of Anthropology.

E. Leland Webber, *Director*
Chicago Natural History Museum

FOREWORD

I was fortunate some years ago in being able to visit Captain Fuller several times, once in company with William Fagg, in order to examine and photograph for the Benin History Scheme's records his very large and fine collection of Benin antiquities. The business of photographing was done in the garden on an improvised table, with an old shed as background, outside the window of one of the rooms in which he kept his collections. I recall his enthusiasm and interest for the work at hand as he brought out, or passed out of the window, piece after piece to be photographed, discussing the merits of a particular specimen or pointing out some unusual feature. After an afternoon's work, we would adjourn to the sitting room to continue talking with Mrs. Fuller over a typical English tea. It has been a most pleasurable experience to work again with such a fine collection but particularly when joined with another of merit and range. In this respect I have been fortunate in working so closely with Mr. Phillip Lewis and in being able to discuss with him many aspects of Benin art whether general or minutely specific, such as the identity of a particular feature. The burden of editing the manuscript has perforce fallen on him. I wish to record my thanks to him, to Dr. Donald Collier, and to the Director, E. Leland Webber, with all of whom it has been a pleasure to work.

Information in this catalogue stems from work done for the Benin History Scheme directed by Dr. K. O. Dike, Principal of the University College, Ibadan, Nigeria. This research scheme was sponsored by the Nigerian Government, the British Government (C.D.&W.), and the Carnegie Corporation of New York. I wish to thank Dr. Dike for being able to use the Scheme's materials and photographs.

My special thanks are due my colleague, Dr. Bradbury, who knows Edo culture better than anyone. I was fortunate to work with him on the Benin Scheme and am grateful for the many things I learned from him. For many years I have talked frequently about Benin art with William Fagg and have greatly benefited from ideas and information so freely given from his encyclopedic knowledge of Benin and African art.

In the course of my work on Benin art, I have visited many museums and collectors who have always so kindly given me facilities to examine and photograph their specimens. I wish to record my thanks to them for the invaluable data they have enabled me to collect.

While working in Benin with Dr.

Bradbury, His Highness Akenzua II, the Oba of Benin, was always graciously informative about Benin culture. I also learned much while in Benin City from Chief Ine, chief of the Brassworkers.

I am grateful for assistance from Mr. M. Hill, Mrs. Bonelli, and the National Science Foundation, from which I hold a grant at Southern Illinois University to continue research in Benin art. Southern Illinois University has kindly permitted me to help the Chicago Natural History Museum with this exhibition of the art of Benin.

PHILIP J. C. DARK
Professor of Anthropology
Southern Illinois University

THE ART OF BENIN

An Introduction to Its Discovery and Collection

Benin City is in Western Nigeria. It has a population of over 50,000 people. It is growing, changing. It is a city of size, but it has been so for a long time. Early travelers have written of the impression its size has made on them, of its orderliness, of the power and sway of its king.[1] In the fifteenth and sixteenth centuries the kingdom of Benin encompassed territory extending five hundred miles from east to west.[2] Over this territory ruled the king of Benin, the Oba, as absolute monarch from his palace in Benin City. The palace was the hub of the kingdom, whence all affairs were regulated.

Benin City is in the high tropical forest, which stretches east and west, and to the south where it joins the mangrove swamps of the Niger Delta. To the north and northeast this forest changes to orchard scrub and the land to high rocky outcroppings. Where this change takes place is the northernmost frontier of the kingdom of Benin at its greatest extent.

Though shrunk in space, the kingdom of Benin is important in modern Nigeria. Its king, His Highness Akenzua II, the Oba of Benin, is still spiritual ruler over some 200,000 Edo-speaking peoples even if he no longer has absolute political power.[3]

In the Western world Benin has been famous for its art for the last sixty-five years. This art, however, has a much longer history. The examples of it which survive to us were produced over a long period—certainly over the last five centuries, perhaps even longer. The chronology of Benin art is at present inexact. Here and there are one or two time markers, but the current dating of specimens rests largely on a relative time scale.[4] Even when further research has been done, the chronicle of artistic achievements will probably continue to rest on a relative chronology. It should be remembered that much of African art is today of the period of the past. Though all behavior and its results are past, our increasing exposure to African works of art, through museum collections and exhibitions, does perhaps make us regard what we see as of the present. We are, however, in

1. E.g., The Chronicler D. R., 1604, *vide* Roth, 1903: 157–59; and Dapper, 1668, *vide ibid.* 11.

A few Edo words have of necessity been used in this Catalogue, but with an English spelling which is a rather rough approximation to their actual pronunciation.

2. *Vide* remarks by Bradbury, 1957: 21.

3. *Ibid.* 18.

4. For discussions of the chronology of Benin art and history, *vide*, e.g., Elisofon and Fagg, 1958, Forman, W. and B., and Dark, 1960, and Bradbury's (1959) consideration of the evidence at present available.

many instances seeing the end products of a series of artistic traditions, some of great depth. The elongated sculptural forms of the Sudan, which are of such current aesthetic appeal, the humanistic masks of Southern Nigeria, figure carvings from the Congo, some of which express so forcefully the solemnity of princely power or the eternal sadness of women's travails—all these forms and others we have come to accept as works of art in our expanded view of the great arts of the world. The anthropologist and the art historian are addressing themselves more and more to the study of these African works of art and are anxiously attempting to document them with the same thoroughness which they have given to other art traditions, realizing that the cultural contexts of such works are slipping away from us or have passed with little likelihood of reconstruction.

The student of African art is frequently limited to a short time depth in any historical reconstruction he may attempt. There are, however, exceptions, such as the art of the Bakuba, the arts of Ife and Nok, and the art of Benin, which take us back much further in time than does the material we have for most other African cultures south of the Sahara. But examples of Nok art are part of the archeological record with no direct continuity to the present, as with Zimbabwe. Nor do the fine bronzes and terracottas of Ife, on which the fame of Ife art rests, span a definitely known period with which we have direct ties. The objects of Benin art, since its dis-

covery in 1897, have frequently been referred to as the antiquities of Benin and are perhaps generally thought of more in this context of antiquities, as are the bronzes of Ife, than as falling in the contemporary context of African art in general. But the Benin artistic tradition, though changed, has retained its continuity through time right up to the present.

Examples of African art of relatively early date are to be found in museum collections, but they are generally single items. There is, for example, a beautiful Yoruba carving of a kneeling male figure holding a staff in the Royal Albert Museum, Exeter, England, which was given to the Museum by the Reverend H. Townsend. The Reverend Townsend was in Nigeria in the 1840's (?). This specimen, which comes from Abeokuta, was given to the Museum in the 1860's. Ivory carvings of African origin were finding their way into museums in the last century. But earlier than this such carvings existed in the cabinets of the connoisseur and the curio-seeker. The Museum der Stadt, Ulm, has a number of ivory pieces of African execution or influence, which are recorded by Christopher Weichmann in a catalogue of 1659. An edition of this catalogue, published in 1716, refers to two arm rings of ivory, which suggest close affinities with ivory carving from Owo and relationships with Benin bronze work, notably the rare neck rings with relief figures of bound and gagged prisoners being pecked by carrion. Other ivory carvings of debatable provenience and origin but with a strangely African flavor, for which

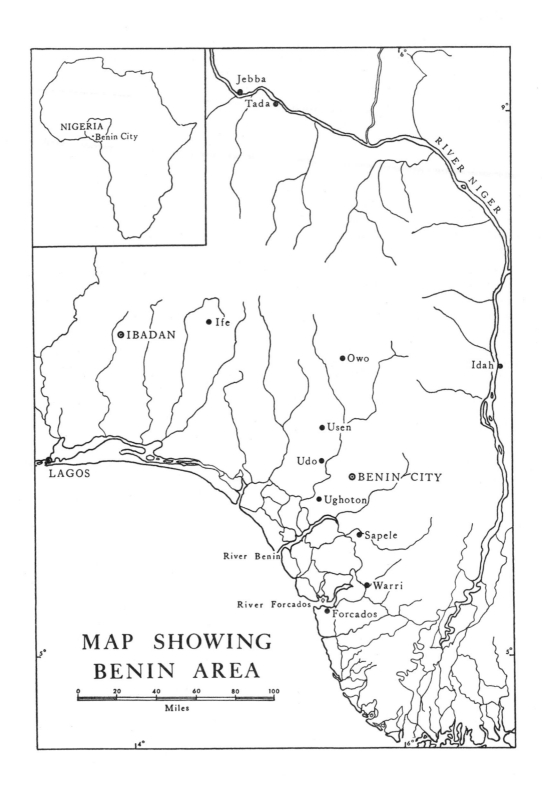

Jebba
Tada

NIGERIA
Benin City

RIVER NIGER

Ife

⊙ IBADAN

●Owo

Idah●

●Usen

Udo●

⊙ BENIN CITY

LAGOS

●Ughoton

●Sapele

River Benin

●Warri

River Forcados

Forcados

MAP SHOWING
BENIN AREA

0   20   40   60   80   100
Miles

William Fagg has aptly coined the term "Afro-Portuguese,"[5] appear in Europe at a still earlier date.[6] But, in spite of its long period of production, no object of Benin art is definitely known to have been in Europe before 1897, the year of the British Punitive Expedition against Benin.[7]

An expedition against Benin was mounted by the British in reprisal for the murder in January, 1897, of the vice-consul of the Oil Rivers Protectorate and his party of Europeans and Jekri porters, who were on their way to visit the king of Benin in order to consider agreements, made earlier, to trade in the area. After severe fighting, the British captured the city of Benin on February 17, 1897. In the course of restoring order to the city, the bronze memorial heads, the bronze plaques, figures in bronze and many other bronze objects, the ivory carvings, and the carvings in wood with which we are now familiar were all brought together and shipped back with the expedition, the main body

of which withdrew from the city on February 22. Once in London, the loot was sold by the Foreign Office.

The impetus to buy these remarkable objects from Benin must have stemmed from several sources. The murder of British Vice-Consul Phillips and most of his party and accompanying porters when on a peaceful visit to the king—even if made at an inopportune moment and contrary to local advice—and the subsequent remarkably rapid reaction of the British Government in mounting a punitive expedition caused quite a public stir. When the members of the expedition found in Benin City the results of the king's annual sacrifices to his ancestors in the form of human remains, Benin became known as the City of Blood[8] and attracted the usual public interest in the sensational.

Members of the expedition, scholars, and collectors recognized at once the technical mastery and artistic excellence of the objects brought back to England. It is, perhaps, worthy of note that the last thirty or forty years of the nineteenth century saw an ever increasing interest in and appreciation of works of art from lands distant to western Europe. Benin art was a major discovery.

One or two articles appeared on Benin art very shortly after the expedition, in 1897. One of these was by Dr. Forbes (1897), the director of the City of Liverpool Public Museums, who was one of the first scholars to take a keen interest in Benin art and

5. *Vide* Fagg and Forman, 1959.

6. Denise Paulme, 1956: 71, cites a reference to a work of 1620 by Michael Praetorius as depicting an ivory trumpet from Benin. The object illustrated cannot definitely be ascribed to Benin.

7. In the Free Public Museums, Liverpool, England, there is a specimen which may have come from Benin before 1897. The entry in the stock book reads: "9.7.95.7 Fan made of hide on the front a design in red worsted, the handle formed of strips of platted leather. L. 18½". Collected and presented by Ridyard, Niger River, West Africa." The Museums particularly, because of Liverpool's active trade with Nigerian ports for so many years, would have been in a good position to have acquired ethnographical material emanating from the Benin region.

8. The title of Commander R. H. Bacon's (1897) book. Commander Bacon was Chief of Intelligence on the Expedition.

who played an active role in the early formation of the then Field Museum's collection. W. D. Webster (1898), one of the leading dealers in primitive works of art at the end of the last century and the beginning of the present one, was quick to acquire specimens from Benin and include them in his famous catalogues. Concurrently with the first studies of the art appeared descriptions of Benin, its people, and the Benin massacre and punitive expedition—Bacon (1897), Boisragon (1897), and Pinnock (1897). Captain Boisragon was one of the two Europeans to escape the massacre, and his book went into a second edition in 1898. In the next two years, 1898–99, Forbes continued to publish, as did also such English scholars as C. H. Read, O. M. Dalton, and H. Ling Roth. In Germany, during the same two years, scholars began to publish their observations on the collections so rapidly and astutely acquired from the sale in London of the antiquities from Benin. W. Foy wrote from Dresden, Karl von Hagen from Hamburg, Felix von Luschan from Berlin, and Franz Heger from Vienna. The fine museums in all these four cities acquired large collections of major importance. The most notable publication of this time was that of Read and Dalton (1899), describing the collection acquired by the British Museum, which formed the foundation of the extensive collections made subsequently. This volume is noteworthy for the excellence of its plates, which illustrate, particularly, a wide variety of bronze plaques. In 1900 the aforementioned scholars continued their writings and were joined by others. The outstanding work of the year was the magnificent volume put out by Lieutenant General Lane Fox Pitt-Rivers (1900), who bought a wide range of Benin objects for inclusion in the large museum on his private estate at Farnham, Dorset, where several halls of outstanding ethnographical material from the world are matched by a number of halls in which complete reconstructions of his excavations in southern England are displayed with all the scientific exactitude which he demanded of the archeologist.

Many more studies were to follow in the years after 1900. There is no period of any length up to the present when the interest of the anthropologist, the art historian, and artist has not found expression in print of some interest in Benin art. Of signal note from Europe is Ling Roth's (1903) *Great Benin* and works by von Hagen (1900–1918), Marquart (1913), Struck (1923), and Von Sydow (1938). Von Luschan wrote a number of articles and studies of Benin art, but his *Altertümer von Benin* (1919) remains the monumental compendium on the subject. Since the second World War, William Fagg has been the leading scholar in the study of Benin art. In this country the names of H. U. Hall, E. A. Hooton, and J. J. Sweeney spring to mind as having been particularly concerned with our subject. Hall wrote on the splendid University Museum collections in Philadelphia, and Hooton on the small collection in the Peabody Museum, Harvard University.

But many writings on Benin art

depended a great deal on the collections made. The objects sold in 1897 were bought by dealers, museums, and private collectors.

The artistic discernment of some senior members of the expedition is certainly matched by contemporary aesthetic values as to good and bad art and what is a good Benin piece and what is not. Sir Ralph Moor was consul-general and administrator-general of the then Niger Coast Protectorate. At his death several of the finest pieces of Benin art passed to a relative from whom Professor Seligman obtained the two finest of Benin ivory masks and two of the finest ivory armlets ever made at Benin.[9] Through Professor Seligman's good offices, one of the masks and the two armlets passed to the British Museum; the other mask remained for many years in Mrs. Seligman's hands until sold to the Museum of Primitive Art, New York, for the highest price ever paid for a Benin piece, namely, $56,000.[10] Admiral Brian Egerton, the son of the late Admiral Sir George Egerton, who was a captain in the Royal Navy and second in command of the expedition, has retained almost intact the fine collection made by his father. The collection made by Dr. R. Allman, who was principal medical officer of the expedition and of the Niger Coast Protectorate from 1891 to 1905, was finally sold by Mr. R. B. Allman at Sotheby's on June 27, 1960. Most of the collections made by other members appear to have been sold or do-

nated to museums. The late Captain Fuller, as the catalogue shows, bought some pieces from Mr. Locke, who, with Captain Boisragon, were the only two Europeans to survive the massacre.

Several dealers bought widely when the market for Benin art opened. Outstanding was W. D. Webster. There are few museum catalogues which do not bear his name. Some other well-known dealers who were on the scene early and who, like Webster, did not confine their ethnographical interests to Benin were Miss Cutter (who subsequently became Webster's partner), Stevens, Oldman, H. Bey, and Umlauff. London companies, such as Fenton and Sons, Christie, Manson and Woods, and Hale and Son, are referred to in catalogues. Though some museums received gifts from members of the expedition or from donors who had bought from dealers —Miss Mary Kingsley, for example gave several pieces to the Pitt-Rivers Museum, Oxford University—most museums bought their collections.

As far as can be ascertained, the British Museum was the first to obtain examples of Benin art. The earliest date of acquisition would appear to be June 18, 1897, just under four months from the time the main party of the expedition withdrew from Benin. Ling Roth (1903: App. IV), in an appendix to his book *Great Benin*, held forth with some bitterness about the lack of adequate funds being available to the British Museum to secure proper collections commensurate with its national stature. Fortunately, however, the foundations of

9. Fagg, 1957.

10. See the *Daily Telegraph* (London), Feb. 6, 1958.

11

the British Museum's Benin collections were set at this time and included a magnificent range of bronze plaques, which, together with subsequent augmentations, forms the finest and largest single collection of this type of object. Indeed, the British Museum collections of Benin art have been increased gradually by acquisitions and gifts so that they are the largest and most widely representative in the world, certainly larger than the Berlin collection at the time of its maximum size, which was before the second World War, when it numbered some 594 pieces.[11] Notable gifts have been made by such as Captain Cockburn, a member of the expedition, who presented specimens to the British Museum in the month of June, 1897 (referred to above), Mrs. Beasley, and the Wellcome Foundation. From 1934 until November 20, 1961, the Museum had the advantage of having on loan the small but fine collection of some twenty pieces belonging to J. S. Howe, who had inherited it from Dr. J. P. Howe, a member of the expedition.[12]

The Museum für Völkerkunde, Berlin-Dahlem, began buying examples of Benin art in 1897 and was very actively acquiring pieces in the years 1898, 1899, and 1900. By 1901 a large portion of its former large collection was established, though it continued to obtain pieces up to 1940. The Royal Scottish Museum, Edinburgh, likewise started its collection in 1897 and continued to make acquisitions in subsequent years. The Museum für Kunst und Gewerbe, Hamburg, bought a bronze head in 1897, and the Rijksmuseum voor Volkenkunde, Leiden, started its collection in the same year. Examples of other museums active in these first years after 1897 are the Glasgow Art Gallery and Museum and the Museum für Völkerkunde, Hamburg, in 1898. The National Museum, Copenhagen, bought several pieces from Webster in 1899. The famous Vienna collection at the Museum für Völkerkunde was likewise started in the same year by a gift of 76 pieces from Georg Haas, and the Linden Museum, Stuttgart, collection, similarly, by a gift of specimens from Karl Knorr. The Statens Ethnografiska Museet, Stockholm, started its collection in 1900, though the major portion was acquired in 1907.

The foundations of the large collection in the Pitt-Rivers Museum, Oxford University, were also laid in 1900. The first Benin accession number at the Rautenstrauch-Joest Museum, Cologne, is November 20, 1901. In the next year, the large collection at the Museum of Archaeology and Ethnology, Cambridge University, was started, though one or two pieces may have been bought from Webster in 1899.

In view of the fantastically high prices being paid today for works of art, no matter from what art tradition they may come, it is perhaps interesting to consider what prices were being paid for objects of Benin art when they first became available. By reference to museum catalogues and by making a fair comparison with the objects represented in the plates of

11. Krieger, 1957.

12. Sotheby & Co., 1961.

this exhibition catalogue, one can say that a plaque such as 272 (Plate XIII) would have fetched about $14.00, though a plaque such as 260 (Plate XLI) somewhat more, perhaps $40.00. An idiophone such as 205 or 204 (Plate V) would have fetched about $12.00. Bronze armlets would vary from $3.00 to $7.00 (e.g., 1–5, 10–11, 18–23, 76). A figure such as that of the king pictured in Plate XXIV (103) would have cost perhaps $140.00, and a fine tusk, in 1901, such as that in Plate XVII, over $200.00 at auction. A record for 1898 shows that a bronze head, such as in Plate XXXV, fetched $23.00 at auction, and a record for 1903 shows that $42.00 was paid for a head as fine as the "Udo" head (126, Plate XIII) of the Fuller Collection. The then Field Museum paid $450 in 1899 for two plaques (250 and 273), costing $90.00, two figures of a king (103 and 104), costing $90, and three memorial heads (125, 122, and 121), costing $270.00. These objects were obtained through the good offices of Dr. H. O. Forbes, director of the Free Public Museums, Liverpool. Dr. Forbes was one of the first to acquire examples of Benin art. The records show that he was first buying in October, 1897, and continued to acquire specimens in the following years for the Liverpool Museums. Unfortunately, many items listed in the Museums' catalogues were destroyed by bombs in the second World War.

The early acquisition by the Field Columbian Museum of specimens of Benin art was due to the initiative of its active chief curator of anthropology, Dr. Dorsey. Dorsey was in England in 1898 and, on his return to the States, directed a letter, dated November 19, to Mr. F. J. V. Skiff, who was at that time director of the Museum. In that letter he wrote: "While in Liverpool in the Free Public Museum, I saw for the first time a number of the bronze objects and carved elephant tusks from Benin, West Africa; later on in my visit to other European Museums, I saw a large number of additional specimens especially in Berlin where they now have the largest collection in existence. These bronze casts and carved elephant tusks are probably the most remarkable specimens which have ever been brought out of Africa. Their presence at Benin was probably unknown until about three years ago when the first of these wonderful specimens of Negro workmanship was brought to the attention of the anthropologists of Europe. At the British Association meeting at Bristol, I talked with Dr. H. O. Forbes, the well-known ethnologist of the South Seas, and Director of the Liverpool Museum, in regard to the possibility of acquiring some of these specimens for the Field Columbian Museum. He informed me that the visible supply had been completely absorbed by European museums, but that a consignment was shortly expected in Liverpool, and inasmuch as his Museum could not afford to make additional purchases he would be glad to secure some for the Field Columbian Museum."

Previous to this letter, but after Dorsey's meeting with Forbes at Bristol, Forbes had first refusal on the consignment to a firm in Liverpool and bought the specimens for the Field Museum, though, apparently, without arrangements to do so being quite clear between him and Dorsey. Forbes's action, however, prevented a Hamburg museum, which had made a bid for the specimens, from purchasing them. The first acquisition (Acc. 617) of the Field Museum was dispatched by Forbes on April 19, 1899, and received by the Museum on June 3. The sum of £125 was paid in July.

With characteristic energy, Dorsey concluded the letter referred to above by pressing for the further acquisition of objects of Benin art: "It will be noticed that should it be decided to make this purchase the Museum will not be in possession of any of the carved elephant tusks. These are fully as remarkable from their point of view as the bronze, and it seems to me that we should possess at least four or five. In the Crystal Palace of London are two such specimens excellently well preserved, although probably over 300 years of age, for which a price of 100 pounds is asked: I also saw in the Umlauff Museum of Hamburg three additional specimens the price of which was 4,000 marks. I also recommend that these five specimens be secured. With these three collections united we would have probably the third largest collection of Benin objects in the world, and the only collection on this side of the Atlantic Ocean."

Forbes was away in Socotra during the winter of 1898–99, but in May wrote to Dorsey that good pieces were still being offered to him but were becoming rarer. He indicated that he would be happy to obtain further specimens if the Field Museum so desired. Forbes's offer was not, however, taken up, and the next accessions (Acc. 808) made came from a different source and two years later. Four bronze memorial heads (120, 123, 124, and 131) were purchased for $585.60, though not received by the Museum until April 5, 1902. Dorsey objected to this sum being spent on heads which were so similar to the ones acquired in 1899. In a letter of November 27, 1901, to the director he wrote: "The sum of $585.00 could have been much more advantageously expended for that class of Benin art work on objects not now adequately represented in our collection. I refer more particularly to the carved elephant tusks for which these bronze heads served as receptacles. As a matter of fact, a recommendation of mine that one of these wonderfully carved tusks be purchased, was denied by you." Dorsey's wish for a finely carved tusk and for a wider representation of Benin specimens was, however, to be fulfilled in the following years. In fact, two years later, in 1904, he was to get three examples of such tusks and through the same hands as those which had obtained the heads to which he objected.

In February, 1904, Mr. Ayer bought from M. W. Edgley the three large carved tusks (306, 308, and 307, Plates XVII, XXIX, and XL) of the Museum's collection for £150 ($750) (Acc. 862), remarking in a letter from the Hotel Cecil in London to the director that they were *"very cheap"* and hoping that "Mr. Dorsey would install them with the heads and other Benin bronzes upon arrival." The Museum received them on May 3.

Over the next three years the Museum was able to fulfill Dorsey's wish for a wider representation of Benin material. From 1905 to 1907 a considerable number of objects were obtained from W. D. Webster in England. Dorsey was in London in 1905 and, on his return, wrote in July to the director that there was an opportunity of obtaining "a lot of rare specimens at an exceptionally low Price," since Webster and Miss Cutter were merging their businesses. "I, therefore," Dorsey wrote, "availed myself of the opportunity of the presence of Dr. Haddon of Cambridge, and examined the collections of Webster and Cutter with great care, and purchased, subject to your approval, specimens as per attached memorandum, amounting in all to pounds 226, sh. 19. . . . I have the honor to recommend that this sum be appropriated for the purchase of these specimens, and that as soon as may be convenient you forward to Miss E. Cutter, 36 Great Russell Street, London, shipping directions for this collection. As you will see by even a superficial examination of the list, the objects which I selected are all of importance and of exceptional merit, and all practically without exception are such that it would be impossible to secure in the field. I consider it extremely fortunate that we should have the opportunity of securing such

a collection at such a reasonable price."

Four specimens (Acc. 963) were received on October 11 and 122 (Acc. 976) on November 28. On the latter date Webster was paid £583.12.0 for 99 specimens. Earlier in the same month, Miss Cutter wrote that she had a chance of obtaining some exceptionally fine pieces "which belong to an officer who left them in Africa having been ordered to the Far East." Among the items she referred to were two bronze stools, three bronze figures, and a group of figures on a stand. To secure these pieces, Miss Cutter requested financial support by return, "otherwise they will go to Germany." Alas, a great opportunity was missed, for the pieces in question were of the finest examples of the Benin brass-casters' art. These pieces were, in all probability, the property of Sir Ralph Moor, consul-general and administrator-general of the then Niger Coast Protectorate, for Ling Roth had the two bronze stools on loan from Sir Ralph Moor at the Bankfield Museum, Halifax. He tried to raise the money to purchase them but failed. The stools and other pieces were sent to Stevens for sale and were bought in 1905 by the Museum für Völkerkunde, Berlin.

On January 2 and June 20, 1906, Webster, on his own initiative, sent, on approval, to the Field Museum two collections which comprised a wide variety of ethnographical specimens from such areas as Polynesia, Melanesia, and Australia as well as from Benin. Dr. Dorsey went through the collections sent by Webster but was reluctant to ask for an appropriation to buy those pieces he would like to have had. He suggested to Webster that the material either be returned to him or be left at the Museum for a period while he, Dorsey, set about inducing the Museum to buy it. The months of 1906 stretched into 1907; the director was away; even at the leisurely pace at which affairs were conducted in those days, Webster became anxious. On December 18, 1906, Dorsey wrote Webster that he was having difficulty promoting the funds necessary to buy the two collections. On March 29, 1907, he again indicated his difficulty in finding money for payment; but, finally, on October 22, the sum of £700 was sent to Webster. The two collections contained 35 items from Benin (Acc. 1018). The prices paid for individual items are perhaps cause for reflection. The bronze plaque, 269, depicting two snakes, cost $35.00. The plaque (270) on which is pictured a fish cost $21.00. The round kola-nut box (45), which is partly covered with beaten brass, cost $29.00. Bronze bells were priced at $8.00–$10.00 and bronze armlets at $3.00–$4.00.

A gap of twenty-two years followed the accessions made from Webster and the acquisitions made by Dr. Hambly, Curator of African Ethnology. In 1928–29 Dr. Hambly made an expedition to Angola and, on his way back to the States, a field trip through Nigeria. On this field trip he collected, among many other African pieces, some examples of carvings and castings from Benin made after 1897, which were accessioned in 1929.

The only other example of Benin workmanship obtained by the Museum was a wooden cock (84) acquired in 1961.

Though museums have played an outstanding role in the acquisition and preservation of works of art from Benin, one or two individual collectors stand out equally from the point of view of both the size of the collections they made and the range of representation of types of objects. Reference has already been made to Lieutenant General Pitt-Rivers and the collections of ethnological and archeological materials he made and housed in his private museum at Farnham, Dorset. Pitt-Rivers would appear to have bought a number of pieces direct from the Foreign Office, as painted numbers on certain specimens would seem to derive from that office. As well, he bought from Webster and others. In his book (1900), he illustrated some 227 Benin objects, but, in addition, he acquired some 19 pieces not included in his book.

Dr. F. Roth, who was one of the surgeons on the expedition, was the brother of H. Ling Roth, the honorary curator of the Bankfield Museum, Halifax, and one of the scholars most active in research into the history of the culture of Benin from the time of its "discovery" in 1897. Unlike his brother, Ling Roth never visited Benin, but he was busily engaged from the time of the return of the expedition in compiling a record of its history and customs from accounts of visitors through the centuries from earliest contact times to 1897. He also participated in the sales of Benin objects, although he acquired but a few examples of Benin art at Halifax, probably due to lack of funds. It may be that the pieces he sold were acquired from members of the expedition or from his brother. Captain Fuller was to obtain a few fine pieces from him.

Captain Fuller first started his collection of Benin specimens in 1902. In that year, according to the records he has left us, he acquired the *ada* (324) and the *ebē* (315). From that time on, as can be seen from the Catalogue of the collections, he continued to add to his collection. In 1905(?) he bought the plaque of a snake (267, Plate VII) with the rare background of a circle with a cross in it. Throughout the twenties and thirties he made many acquisitions. The last recorded date of accession is March 16, 1948, when he bought several examples of weapons.

The Fuller Collection is widely representative but selective. Not only did Captain Fuller have a good eye for a good piece but he was a connoisseur of material culture with a deep interest in both technical processes and the variety of man's products. Though sometimes collecting a number of pieces of a similar type, he would buy a further example because it had some unusual feature. In this respect, his collection of weapons is of interest, containing examples of both ceremonial and functional swords of different kinds and four examples of shields which are rare. His collection of fans, ten in number, must be the largest single one of its kind. Some of his pieces are representative of the highest point in artistic achievement in the Benin area, notably the unusual, very finely cast head (117, Plate VI) and the ivory medicine horn (151, Plate XLVII), which shows the excellence of the carver's skill. Like many connoisseurs, the rare item attracted him. Item 282 is a "rivet" from a hole in a plaque; Items 340 and 341 are shrapnel charges: "such as this was fired from cannon obtained from Portuguese."

Captain Fuller is, perhaps, known best for his very large and excellent collection of Oceanian art, which was acquired by Chicago Natural History Museum in 1958; his unique library on Oceania, with its many rare editions; and a few Benin pieces, which, from time to time, have appeared in exhibitions and been illustrated in a few books. It is not perhaps widely known that the Fuller Benin Collection is one of the largest of all. It is generally assumed that, before the second World War, the collections of the Museum für Völkerkunde, Berlin-Dahlem, were the largest, numbering 594 examples, though it seems likely that the British Museum collections would have been as large if a count had been recorded. With the sad loss of the Berlin specimens owing to the war and the consequent reduction to 181 pieces, Berlin is exceeded by several collections. The British Museum has continued to make accessions and surpasses in size that of Berlin before the war. The Fuller Collection of Benin art consists of 191 items, and, in addition, 9 items are included in this Catalogue, 2 of which may well be Benin work. As far as is known, the collection is exceeded in quanitity of specimens only by the British Museum; the Museum of Archaeology and Ethnology, Cambridge University; the Museum für Völkerkunde, Hamburg; the Pitt-Rivers Museum, Farnham; the Benin Museum and the Nigerian Museum, Lagos. Close to the Fuller Collection are those of the Museum für Völkerkunde, Vienna; the Pitt-Rivers Museum, Oxford University; and the University Museum, Philadelphia; that of the Chicago Natural History Museum contains the same number of pieces as the Fuller Collection.

It should not be thought that the collections of Benin art now present in the exhibition cases and stores of museums or cherished by the private collector all stem from the time of the expedition. Some objects escaped the hands of the soldiers and sailors who marched on Benin. Others were collected by expatriates resident on various duties in Nigeria and still others by scholars in the course of scientific expeditions. In the Pitt-Rivers Museum, Oxford University, is a "very fine plaque of bronze cast by the *cire-perdue* process. It was hidden away from our soldiers after the capture of Benin on the Punitive Expedition of 1897, and was brought to Lagos by a native trading woman from whom it was obtained by Mr. Embury." With this entry in the catalogue of the Pitt-Rivers Museum at Oxford it is also recorded that this plaque was given to the museum in February, 1907. Both the Pitt-Rivers Museum at Oxford and the Museum of Archaeology and Ethnology at Cambridge obtained material from 1909 to 1912 collected by N. W. Thomas in the Benin area. The Pitt-Rivers Museum at Oxford acquired specimens from P. Amaury Talbot in 1921 and from M. D. W. Jeffreys in 1931–32, both of whom conducted anthropological investigations in Southern Nigeria. Until dispersal after the second World War of much of its fine ethnographical collections, the Wellcome Historical Medical Museum had a large number of examples of Benin workmanship. Some of these objects were obtained by Mr. H. Nevins, who was a district officer in the Benin Division in 1927.

Of all the examples of Benin art collected or assembled after the 1897 exodus, two of the most interesting and largest collections made are those in the Benin Museum and the Nigerian Museum, Lagos. In the Benin Museum are gathered over three hundred examples of the ancient art, together with works made in this century. This fine assemblage was made possible principally by the King of Benin and by certain chiefs, who gave specimens to the Museum. Since then, the collections have been augmented by local purchases by the Department of Antiquities. At Lagos, on the other hand, although the collections of the Nigerian Museum contain examples of works obtained locally, many of the pieces had to be sought outside Nigeria and bought in order to return to their country of origin. Happily, through the discernment of the Antiquities Commission and its officers, Nigeria now has some of the finest examples of Benin art ever produced.

Today, objects of Benin art of early

periods are rare items for the museum or collector. From time to time a few specimens are sold when they appear at auction, as an old collection, often from the family of a member of the expedition. But it must not be thought that Benin art ceased at the end of the last century. The brass-casters and carvers are still at work, and examples of their skill are bought by both Europeans and Africans. Though the subject matter has changed and the objects produced are not such great works of art as those made in earlier times, the style is recognizable, and the artist continues to be as much a professional as his forebears. Some of the craftsmen of Benin have had to abandon their calling: the demand for their skill is no longer present. They have had to turn to other pursuits; for example, the carver has turned carpenter and cabinetmaker. Benin art was essentially a court art, and the major part of its production was consumed by the king and the elaborate hierarchies of chiefs. The demands on the artist have changed—in fact, they have lessened so greatly in many instances that many traditional crafts have ceased. The sons of craftsmen who would normally have followed in their fathers' footsteps have had to turn to more rewarding means of obtaining a livelihood.

Formally, the works of art required by the king and chiefs were made by craftsmen who were members of traditional ward guilds. Each guild had its special ward, or location, in the city where its members lived and worked. The artists were honored members of society and affiliated to the palace organization. Many of them held chiefly titles of importance; some of these titles were hereditary and passed from father to eldest son. The present chief of the brassworkers at Benin is the direct descendant of Iguegha, whom the Oni of Ife sent, at the request of Oba Oguola, to teach the art of casting bronze to the people of Benin.

The works of art of Benin which have the greatest appeal to us were made by the brassworkers. It is common practice to refer to the objects they made as bronze, but, in fact, owing to variations in the proportions of the metals used and impurities, it is improbable that any true bronzes were cast. An item in the Fuller Collection (280), a piece of the flange of a plaque, has been filed down along the edge and demonstrates very clearly the brilliant color of fresh metal metal which we normally would see colored with the red earth of Benin or the patina of age. The brassworkers at Benin used the technique of lost wax casting—a technique known relatively early in the development of metallurgical techniques by man and probably used in Egypt in the seventeenth century B.C. The technique is still used in Benin, and, when Dr. Hambly was there in 1929, he collected a wax model (348), a mold (349), and the finished brass model (352) as illustrative of the stages in the process. The principles of the technique are generally widely known,[13] but it should be noted that there are considerable variations in

13. See Underwood, 1949; Fagg *in* Plass, 1957; Forman, W. and B., and Dark, 1960: 26.

detail of its employment from culture to culture. The Benin brassworker used beeswax to model the form he wished to produce. Generally, this modeling took place on a clay core roughly shaped to the required form. Unlike much casting in bronze, the elaborate system of gates and vents to facilitate the entry of the molten metal to all parts of the form and the expulsion of the gases engendered was not employed. Generally, the Benin brassworker used a single pouring cup from which runners led down to parts of the form to be cast. These runners acted in part as vents, but much of the gases engendered at pouring were absorbed by the investment of clay which contained sufficient carboniferous material for the purpose. The brasscasters in the Cameroons achieve the maximum absorption of gases by the investment by completely inclosing the wax model with a mixture of clay and cow dung. The mixture in the investment is sufficiently charged with carboniferous matter to absorb both the wax and the gases of the molten metal when the mold is fired.[14] Plaque 250 (Plate I) shows a small rod of metal coming from the back of the plaque to the blacksmith's hammer held in the right hand of the central figure. This rod acted both as a support to the hammer, which is in full relief and some distance from the body of the plaque, and as a runner to lead the metal into the form when it was poured. On the large figure of a king (103, Plate XXIV) a similar supporting rod of

14. See Gebauer *in* Bascom and Gebauer, 1953.

metal can be seen to lead from the right shoulder to the ceremonial sword held in the right hand, and from the left shoulder to the scepter. By means of consummate control, at certain periods, the Benin bronze-caster achieved a technical mastery over the lost wax process which has not been surpassed by others. The famous Fuller head (117, Plate VI) is cast to a thinness of 2–3 mm.; the head stands 7¾ inches high but weighs only 3.9 pounds.

Supplies of brass undoubtedly varied in quantity over the centuries. The metal was traded across the Sahara, but the advent of the Portuguese on the coast and, subsequently, other Europeans increased the supply of metal to the brassworker. The variety of cast objects he made can well be gleaned from a perusal of this Catalogue. But, besides objects of cast bronze, the brassworker worked with beaten brass and combinations of certain metals.

Beaten-brass objects, which are represented by several objects in the exhibition and which are listed under "Beaten-Brass Plaques," were made by punching and beating the surface around the motif desired. Dr. Felix Roth in his "Diary of a Surgeon with the Benin Punitive Expedition" (Roth 1903: App. II, p. xi) wrote: "The king's house is rather a marvel— the doors are lined with embossed brass, representing figures, etc., etc., while the roof is formed of sheets of Muntz's metal, and the rafters to support the same artistically carved." It is possible that Items 299–302, two of which are illustrated in Plate XXI, were taken from the palace doors. But, apart from this form of object, beaten-brass shapes were used in combination with cast ones to form lamps (as can be seen in Plate XXXIV) and also to decorate wooden objects. Certain wooden objects, such as the head in 129 (Plate XXXIX) and the kolanut boxes (48 and 45, Plates XXIII and XLIV), were made by the carver and then sent to the brassworker, who decorated them with brass shapes beaten to the surface of the carving and held in place with copper rivets. A number of armlets in the exhibition are made of a beaten-brass strip bent round and held in shape by copper rivets. One or two examples of such armlets show that repairs have been made by riveting in a new piece of beaten brass.

A striking skill of the Benin brassworker was the inlay of cast copper forms in bronze. For example, the rectangular bell, 162, has mud-fish forms of cast copper set in the main body of the object. Similarly, a copper strip is to be seen decorating the nose of the pendant mask (239, Plate XXII). These copper forms were set in the wax model before pouring. Similarly, iron nails were frequently set in the wax model of pendant masks, such as the aforementioned one, and in memorial heads to act as pupils of the eyes in the cast object.

Another technical variation sometimes employed by the brassworker was to cast on iron. The legs of the fine bronze cock (76, Plate X) had iron rods as armatures for the clay core, and the two large figures in the round of kings, 103 (Plate XXIV) and 104, were probably similarly cast. The heavy bracelet, 65, shows three brass heads cast on a ring of iron. Some of the iron weapons included in this exhibition have handles bound by strips of wire of copper or brass and sometimes studded by copper nails—forms of finish applied by the brassworker. The brassworkers also made terracotta heads, one example of which (128, Plate IV) is included in the exhibition. Such heads are very rare.

The carver's skill was also manifest in a wide variety of objects. Unfortunately, on the third day after the expedition's arrival in Benin City, a great conflagration occurred. In consequence, many fine carvings were consumed. Some ivory tusks in collections show their exposure to the fire. Enough carvings, however, remained to show how skillful was the art of the carver. His tools were simple, consisting of adzes and knives, with, at least latterly, chisels of his choice made locally by the blacksmith. The principal materials carved were wood and ivory, although calabash and coconut were also worked. Coconut was used for inlay, such as in the wooden memorial head 129, (Plate XXXIX), where it is set above the eyes to indicate tribal markings. But, as well, coconuts themselves were carved in low relief, principally not by the members of the carver's ward but by the young men, sons of chiefs and important personages, who were the king's personal servants, for example, 357 and 359.

The outstanding works of the carver's art are in ivory. All ivory belonged to the Oba. His mark appears on some small undecorated tusks (e.g., 311, 309, and 310). Three large tusks in this exhibition (illustrated in Plates XVII, XXIX, and XL) are carved in low relief, with a large number of animal forms and figures representing actual and mythical kings. Tusks such as these stood on bronze heads (124, Plate XXXV) on the shrines to past kings, the tips of the tusks leaning against a wall behind the shrine. In some ivory objects, copper wire or pieces of beaten brass or copper were inlaid into the carved forms. The small pendant, 243, provides an example of this inlay technique. But the outstanding Benin carving in ivory in this exhibition is, assuredly, the beautifully controlled, carved medicine horn (151, Plate XLVII) from the Fuller Collection.

The work of the blacksmith finds expression in several items from the two collections: for example, an iron lamp, 150, some weapons with iron blades and barbed spearpoints and three medicine staffs, of which 152 (Plate XXIII) is a fine example. Of the tools used by the blacksmith, which consisted of hammers, tongs, poker, bellows and anvil, only a pair of tongs, 372, occur in the two collections. However, the type of hammer used by the blacksmith is partially represented by the shaft of the hammer held in the right hand by the central figure in Plaque 250 (Plate I); its form is shown by the hammer held in the left hand of the figure (95, Plate XX).

The large collection of fans of the Fuller Collection was made by the leatherworkers, who used to have their own ward. The fans, two of which are illustrated in Plate II, are of cowskin or buckskin, decorated with shapes of red cloth, which is now bought in Lagos. The thread with which the cloth shapes are stitched to the fan is antelope skin. A hole is made with a spike before the stitching with a needle is done. The leatherworker uses scissors, which, he says, he has always had and, therefore, may have had them since the time of the first Portuguese contacts with Benin. The wooden handle, which is covered with skin, the craftsman fashions himself with an adze. In former times the leatherworkers used to make a number of different articles, most interesting of which, perhaps, were the kilts with the projection rising up along the left side of the body. This style of costume is quite often shown on plaques (e.g., 260, Plate XLI), and its form is clearly modeled in the figure of a soldier (102, Plate XLV) and the regal figure (101, Plate XIX), both in the round.

BIBLIOGRAPHY

BACON, COMMANDER R. H.
  1897 *The City of Blood.* London.
BASCOM, WILLIAM R., and PAUL GEBAUER
  1953 *Handbook of West African Art.* Popular Science Handbook No. 5. Milwaukee Public Museum. October.
BOISRAGON, CAPTAIN
  1897 *The Benin Massacre.* London.
BRADBURY, R. E.
  1957 *The Benin Kingdom and the Edo-speaking Peoples of South-Western Nigeria.* London: International African Institute.
  1959 "Chronological Problems in the Study of Benin History," *Journal of the Historical Society of Nigeria,* I, No. 4, 263–86.

DAPPER, O.
1668   *Neuwkeurige Beschrijvinge der Afrikaansche Gewesten.* Amsterdam.

D. R.
1604   (an account of Benin *in* DE BRY, Frankfurt ed., 6th part; see ref. by Roth, 1903: 1).

ELISOFON, ELIOT, and WILLIAM FAGG
1958   *The Sculpture of Africa.* London: Thames & Hudson.

FAGG, WILLIAM
1957   "The Seligman Ivory Mask from Benin," *Man,* No. 143 (August).
1960   *The Epstein Collection of Primitive and Exotic Sculpture.* The Arts Council of Great Britain.
1960   *Nigerian Tribal Art.* The Arts Council of Great Britain.
1961   "Nigeria, 2000 Jahre Plastik," *Katalog William Fagg, Photos Herbert List. Ausstellung von 29 Sept. 1961 bis 7 Januar 1962.* Munich: Städtische Galerie.

FAGG, WILLIAM, and W. and B. FORMAN
1959   *Afro-Portuguese Ivories.* London: Batchworth Press.

FORBES, H. O.
1897   "On a Collection of Cast Metalwork from Benin," *Bulletin of the Liverpool Museums,* I, No. 1, 49 ff.
1899   "Cast Metalwork from Benin," *Bulletin of the Liverpool Museums,* II, 13 ff.

FORMAN, W. and B., and PHILIP DARK
1960   *Benin Art.* London: Batchworth Press Ltd.

FOY, W.
1898   "Ethnographische Objekte von Benin, im Kgl. Ethn. Mus. Dresden," *Dresdener Journal,* No. 152/3.
1900/1 "Zur Frage nach der Herkunft einiger alter Jagdhörner aus Elfenbein: Portugal oder Benin? und Anhang: Bibliografie über Benin," *Abh. u Ber. des Kgl. Zool. u. A. E. Museums* (Dresden), IX, 20–22.

HAGEN, K. VON
1900–1918 *Altertümer von Benin im Museum für Völkerkunde zu Hamburg.* 2 vols. Vol. I, 1900; Vol. II, 1918.

HALL, H. U.
1922   "Great Benin Royal Altar," *Journal of the University of Pennsylvania Museum,* XIII, 105–67.
1924   "African Cups Embodying Human Forms," *The Museum Journal, University Museum* (Philadelphia), September, pp. 190–227.
1926   "An Ivory Standing Cup from Benin," *Journal of the University of Pennsylvania Museum,* XVII, 414–32.
1928   "A Large Drum from Benin," *Journal of the University of Pennsylvania Museum,* XIX, 130–43.

HEGER, FRANZ
1899   *Benin und Seine Altertümer.* Mitt. d. Anthr. Ges. Wien 29, 2–6.

HOOTON, E. A.
1917   *Benin Antiquities in the Peabody Museum.* Harvard African Studies I: 130–46.

KRIEGER, K.
1957   "Das Schicksal der Benin-Sammlung des Berliner Museums für Völkerkunde," *Baessler-Archiv,* Neue Folge, V, 225–32.

LUSCHAN, FELIX VON
1898   "Altertümer von Benin," *Zeitschrift für Ethnologie,* XXX, 146–62.
1899   "Über die alten Handsbeziehungen von Benin," *Verh. des VII intern. Geogr.-Kongresses, Berlin,* pp. 607–12.
1900   "Brühstuck einer Benin-Platte," *Globus,* LXXVI, 306/7.
1901   "Die Karl Knorr'sche Sammlung von-Benin Altertümern in Museum für Länder und Völkerkunde in Stuttgart." In *Jahresbericht 17 und 18 des Württembergischen Vereins für Handelsgeographie, Stuttgart.*

1919 *Die Altertümer von Benin.* 3 Bde. Berlin and Leipzig.

MARQUART, J.
1913 *Die Benin-Sammlung des Reichesmuseums für Völkerkunde im Leiden.* Veröffentlichungen des Reichsmuseums für Völkerkunde in Leiden, Serie 2, No. 7. Leiden: E. J. Brill.

MELZIAN, H.
1937 *A Concise Dictonary of the Bini Language of Southern Nigeria.* London: Kegan Paul, Trench, Trubner & Co., Ltd.

MURRAY, K. C.
1961 "Benin Art." *Nigeria Magazine,* No. 71 (December), pp. 370–78.

PAULME, DENISE
1956 *Les Sculptures de l'Afrique noire.* Paris: Presses Universitaires de France.

PLASS, MARGARET WEBSTER
1957 *Metal Casting on the Guinea Coast. Lost Wax: An Exhibition Arranged by Margaret Webster Plass.* Introduction by WILLIAM FAGG. London: ICA. March.

PINNOCK, J.
1897 "Benin, the Surrounding Country, Inhabitants, Customs, and Trade," *Liverpool Journal of Commerce.*

PITT-RIVERS, LIEUTENANT GENERAL L. F.
1900 *Antique Works of Art from Benin.* London.

PRAETORIUS, MICHAEL
1620 *Syntagma musicum.* Wolfenbüttel: Theatrum Instrumentorum.

RADIN, PAUL, and J. J. SWEENEY
1954 *African Folktales and Sculpture.* Bollingen Series XXXII.

READ, C. H., and O. M. DALTON
1899 *Antiquities from the City of Benin and Other Parts of West Africa in the British Museum.* London.

ROTH, H. LING
1903 *Great Benin: Its Customs, Art and Horrors.* Halifax, England: A. King & Sons, Ltd.

SOTHEBY AND CO.
1961 *Catalogue of African Sculpture, Pre-Columbian Gold Ornaments and North-West American Art.* Mon. November 20.

STRUCK, B.
1923 "Chronologie der Benin-Altertümer." In *Zeitschrift für Ethnologie,* LV, 113–66.

SWEENEY, J. J.
1935 *African Negro Art.* New York: Museum of Modern Art.
1941 *African Bronzes from Ife and Benin.* New York.

SYDOW, EVON VON
1938 "Ancient and Modern Art in Benin City," *Africa,* XI, No. 1 (January), 55–62.

TALBOT, P. A.
1926 *The Peoples of Southern Nigeria.* 4 vols. London.

UNDERWOOD, LEON
1949 *Bronzes of West Africa.* London. Alec Tiranti, Ltd.

WEBSTER, W. D.
1898–1901 *Illustrated Catalogue of Ethnographical Specimens . . . on Sale, Oxford House, Bicester, Oxon.* Vol. III, Nos. 18–23; Vol. IV, Nos. 24–27; Vol. V, Nos. 28–31.

SUGGESTED READINGS IN ENGLISH

BRADBURY, R. E.
1957 *The Benin Kingdom and the Edo-speaking Peoples of Southwestern Nigeria.* London: International African Institute.
1959 "Chronological Problems in the Study of Benin History," *Journal of the Historical Society of Nigeria,* I, No. 4, 263–86.

EGHAREVBA, JACOB
1960 *A Short History of Benin.* 3d ed. Ibadan: Ibadan University Press.

ELISOFON, ELIOT, and WILLIAM FAGG
1958 *The Sculpture of Africa*. London: Thames & Hudson.
FORMAN, W. and B., and PHILIP DARK
1960 *Benin Art*. London: Batchworth Press Limited.
ROTH, H. LING
1903 *Great Benin: Its Customs, Art and Horrors*. Halifax (England): A. King & Sons, Ltd.
TALBOT, P. A.
1926 *The Peoples of Southern Nigeria*. 4 vols. London.
UNDERWOOD, LEON
1949 *Bronzes of West Africa*. London: Alec Tiranti, Ltd.

The pieces listed in this section of the Catalogue to the Exhibition belong, except in one instance, to either the Fuller Collection or the Chicago Natural History Museum. The exception is the fine early bronze head, 118, from the City Art Museum, St. Louis, which was loaned through the kindness of the director, Dr. Charles Nagel. The purpose of borrowing this one piece was to be able to show the stylistic development of the bronze heads as it is generally agreed that it took place.

Not all the Benin objects in the two collections are exhibited, but they are all included in the list. Those not on exhibition are marked by an asterisk (*). Included in the list are bronzes which are from the Benin region or have often been considered as Benin workmanship but which cannot so definitely be assigned. It is convenient to consider such objects as belonging to what William Fagg has aptly called "the Lower Niger Bronze Industry" until such time as their proveniences have been determined. Their differentiation from the main body of Benin art rests mainly on stylistic grounds.

Many pieces of the Fuller Collection were labeled by Captain Fuller with the dates on which he acquired them. On some of these labels he noted the date of acquisition, or,

sometimes on a larger tag, he recorded in his precise, neat handwriting from which collection a piece originated and noted his own observations about it. These labeled data are quoted in the list under the appropriate specimens.

Captain Fuller's specimens had no catalogue numbers. In working on Captain Fuller's material some years ago, the writer applied numbers employed in the analysis of Benin art made for the Benin History Scheme. It was decided to use these numbers for this catalogue as easy referents.

Fuller Fuller Collection
CNHM Chicago Natural History Museum

The material of the two collections has been grouped under the following headings and will be found on the Catalogue pages indicated:

ARMLETS

Armlets are of three principal types: carved ivory, cast brass, and beaten brass. A fourth type is represented by 34, which is made up of coils of fiber to which cowrie shells have been sewn. Armlets of ivory are generally carved in low relief, though two notable examples in low and high relief are in the British Museum and were referred to in the introductory essay in reference to Professor Seligman. Armlets of beaten brass are made from one sheet of brass, which is riveted by means of copper rivets. In some instances beaten-brass armlets have the rims turned over a piece of copper or brass wire; in others the rim is just turned over on itself.

On ceremonial occasions, armlets carved of ivory are worn by the Oba; those made from bronze are worn by chiefs. Plaques 250 and 253 provide examples of armlets being worn by a king and a chief, respectively.

Bands of designs run in one of two ways round armlets: first, around the circumference of the armlet; second, up and down the length of the armlet, parallel to the axis of the cylinder. A wide range of designs is used, both representations of people and of animals and various geometric motifs.

1. ARMLET. *Ivory.* L. 5½". Diam. 3⅝". *Fuller.* R.2/5.

Going round the circumference are rows of European heads alternating with cow skulls (or leopard?) which are carved in low relief. Also going round the circumference are four rows of four holes each. There is a hole for the attachment of a coral bead. This armlet is a pair with 2.

2. ARMLET. *Ivory.* L. 5⅝". Diam. 3½". *Fuller.* R.2/6.

Similar to and a pair with 1, but the motifs are more distinct. "Pair of ivory armlets from Benin probably 3 to 4 hundred years old figures much worn with time. Exceedingly rare . . . [corner clipped off tag]. From the collection of Lieut. Col. J. B. Gaskell. 22 February, 1926" (Fuller).

3. ARMLET. *Ivory.* L. 5½". Diam. 3½". *Fuller.* R.2/7.

A very fine example of the Horseman style of ivory armlet. In low relief are two horsemen, each holding a dagger, alternating with two standing figures, each holding a spear with both hands, the figures, however, being the other way up to the horsemen. Above the head of each figure is a small leopard, and above the head of each horseman is a large leopard with, in its mouth, a goat (cf. plaque in the British Museum of a leopard with a goat in its mouth [98.1–15.200], illustrated in Forman, W. and B., and Dark, 1960: Fig. 88). "*Great Benin*. Ivory armlet collected by Dr. J. G. Whittendale, late of Lime House, Bishop's Waltham. 28 April 1917" (Fuller).

4. ARMLET. *Ivory*. L. 5". Diam. 3½". *Fuller*. R.2/8.
A well-worn but good example of the Horseman style of ivory armlet. It shows, in low relief, a similar arrangement of figures to that of 3 above, but has additional motifs filling spaces which, in 3, are left free and balance well the design. The additional motifs are a tortoise and foliage. The two horsemen are each smoking a pipe.

5. ARMLET. *Ivory*. L. 5". Diam. 3¼". *Fuller*. R.2/9.
Though broken in two pieces and well worn, this armlet is bold in design, which consists of six heads of a European and six leopard or cow skulls going round the armlet, alternating in columns of three motifs. "*West Africa*. Benin ivory armlet of great age carved w. 6 European heads, leopards' heads, etc. 15 July 1924" (Fuller).

6. ARMLET *Ivory*. L. 4⅞". Max. Diam. 3". *CNHM* 89690.
Similar to 1 and 2.

7. ARMLET. *Bronze*. L. 5½". Diam. 3⅜". *Fuller*. R.2/1.
Plate XLIII
In low relief are five columns of mud fish alternating in each column and between columns with a simplified, square-shaped motif of a European head. The motifs are facing around the armlet. Between the columns the spaces are filled with a chased floral guilloche motif and stippled marks. A pair with 8.

8. ARMLET. *Bronze*. L. 5⅜". Diam. 3½". *Fuller*. R.2/2.
A pair with 7. "*Benin*. A pair of heavy bronze armlets decorated with catfish and conventionalized European heads. 5 January, 1933" (Fuller).

9. ARMLET. *Bronze*. L. 5⅜". Diam. 3⅝". *Fuller*. R.2/3.
Plate XLIII
In low relief are ten columns of leopard heads alternating with *ebē*, the ceremonial type of sword. The motifs are facing around the armlet.

10. ARMLET. *Bronze*. L. 5¾". Diam. 3¾". *Fuller*. R.2/4.
Plate XLIII
In low relief are five columns of five motifs each. The motifs are the head of a European, a mud fish and a crocodile's head all of which face around the armlet. The motifs are in an alternating arrangement both in a column and around the armlet.

11. ARMLET. *Bronze*. L. 5½". Diam. 3¾". *Fuller*. R.2/17.
The armlet is divided into four panels, each of a figure of a European with a walking stick. The four figures are shown alternating, head up, head down, separated by four panels of pierced interlace. A pair with 12. "IIID/2 16/7/1931" (Fuller).

12. ARMLET. *Bronze*. L. 5⅝". Diam. 3⅜". *Fuller*. R.2/18.
A pair with 11 above. "IIID/2 16/7/ 1931" (Fuller).

13. ARMLET. *Bronze*. L. 5¾". Diam. 3⅝". *Fuller*. R.2/19.
The armlet is decorated with two bands of a chased floral guilloche going round the armlet and alternating with three bands, in relief, of a looped strap motif. Eyelets, for suspension of crotals, are on the two rims at each end. "*Great Benin*. Bronze armlet originally in the Bankfield Museum: Halifax and obtained through H. Ling Roth, the Hon. Curator and author of 'Great Benin' (see 'Great Benin,' fig. 43, p. 33; Pitt-Rivers 'Antique Works of Art from Benin,' fig. 140). 24 July, 1920" (Fuller).

14. Armlet. *Bronze*. L. 4⅛″. Diam. 3½″. *CNHM* 89756.

*

The armlet is decorated with two bands of pierced interlace, going round. Probably a pair with 15.

15. Armlet. *Bronze*. L. 4⅛″. Diam. 3¼″. *CNHM* 89757.

*

Similar to and probably a pair with 14.

16. Armlet. *Bronze*. L. 4⅛″. Diam. 3¾″. *CNHM* 89758.

*

The armlet is decorated with two bands of low relief spirals, the area around each spiral being pierced. There are twelve spirals to a band which goes round the armlet.

17. Armlet. *Bronze*. L. 5⅞″. Diam. 3⅞″. *CNHM* 89759.

Three bands of twelve spiral elements per band, similar to 16 above, go round the armlet but are separated by two bands of pierced interlace. Each rim at each end has eyelets for the suspension of crotals.

18. Armlet. *Brass* (Beaten.) L. 5⅜″. Diam. 3⅜″. *Fuller*. R.2/11.

The surface is decorated with four columns of an angular guilloche design alternating with four columns of a variation on a scale design (cf. a similar design on the kilts of the three figures in plaque 250 [Plate I]). The empty spaces of the designs are stippled.

19. Armlet. *Brass* (Beaten). L. 5½″. Diam. 3½″. *Fuller*. R.2/12.

This armlet was designed, apparently, to have two sets of three panels, alternating, as with 32, but it seems that either the artist miscalculated or, more probably, that the armlet was broken and one panel, in which the design is different from the others, was used as a repair, for it has been riveted in along both edges. Two of the panels each contain the form of a monster, as in 32, the three remaining panels containing octrafoil motifs

separated by two guilloche motifs. Spaces are stippled. *"Benin.* Armlet of thin brass with two debased human figures embossed. An unusual feature is its formation from 2 sheets of metal (see Webster's Catalogue 29, No. 9; 21, Nos. 76, 78, 90; Pitt-Rivers' 'Antique Works of Art,' pl. 45, fig. 349; 25 May, 1928" (Fuller).

20. Armlet. *Brass* (Beaten). L. 5¾″. Diam. 3⅜″. *Fuller*. R.2/13.

*

This armlet is decorated with five bands going round the circumference, in which are guilloche motifs, square panels, each containing a foliate design, and the frontal view of a European head. The European heads alternate up and down.

21. Armlet. *Brass* (Beaten). L. 5⅛″. Diam. 3⅛″. *Fuller*. R.2/14.

*

This is decorated with an all-over scale design. Similar to 23 but with less precision.

22. Armlet. *Brass* (Beaten). L. 5½″. Diam. 3⅛″. *Fuller*. R.2/15.

*

This is decorated with three panels of an angular guilloche design, with all spaces stippled, alternating with three plain panels. Similar to 30. *"Benin.* Armlet of thin embossed brass. The 3 plain panels were probably intended to have figures superimposed like the specimen in Webster's Catalogue 29, fig. 7. 25 May, 1928" (Fuller).

23. Armlet. *Brass* (Beaten). L. 5¼″. Diam. 3¼″. *Fuller*. R.2/16.

*

Similar to 21.

24. Armlet. *Brass* (Beaten) L. 5½″. Diam. 3¼″. *CNHM* 89760.

Decorated with eight panels of geometric and curvilinear designs, including guilloches and scales. A pair with 25(?).

25. Armlet. *Brass* (Beaten). L. 5⅜″. Diam. 3⅛″. *CNHM* 89761.

Similar to and a pair with 24(?).

26. ARMLET. *Brass* (Beaten). L. 5¼″. Diam. 2⅞″. *CNHM* 89762.
*

The decoration is divided into five panels, four of which contain various guilloche designs and the fifth a scale pattern. Spaces are stippled.

27. ARMLET. *Brass* (Beaten). L. 4⅞″. Diam. 3⅜″. *CNHM* 89763.
Decorated with three bands of designs going round the circumference, the innermost one containing a floral guilloche and the outer two a series of plant forms alternating up and down. Spaces are stippled. A pair with 28(?).

28. ARMLET. *Brass* (Beaten). L. 4⅞″. Diam. 3¾″. *CNHM* 89764.
Similar to and a pair with 27(?).

29. ARMLET. *Brass* (Beaten). L. 4⅞″. Diam. 3⅛″. *CNHM* 89765.
*
Similar to 23.

30. ARMLET. *Brass* (Beaten). L. 5½″. Diam. 3″. *CNHM* 89766.
*
Similar to 22.

31. ARMLET. *Brass* (Beaten). L. 4¾″. Diam. 3″. *CNHM* 89767.
*

Decorated with an all-over diamond pattern with the spaces filled with stippling. The rims are formed of separate pieces of brass, turned over each end and fashioned to form a scalloped border with punch marks.

32. ARMLET. *Brass* (Beaten). L. 5⅞″. Diam. 3½″. *CNHM* 89768.
Similar to 19 but a complete piece; thus three panels containing the form of a "monster" alternate with three of a guilloche motif.

33. ARMLET. *Brass* (Beaten). L. 5⅛″. Diam. 3¼″. *CNHM* 89769.
*

This armlet appears to have been repaired by riveting a panel from another armlet to the main portion, which is covered with pierced punch marks, made from the inside, giving the appearance of a cheese grater. The piece used to repair the armlet is of a different quality of brass from the main portion and is decorated with three bands, the innermost of a floral guilloche pattern and the outer two of interlocking scale motifs; spaces are stippled.

34. ARMLET. *Fiber, Cotton, Cowries.* L. 6⅛″. Diam. 4½″. *Fuller.* R.1/80.
This armlet is decorated with cowrie shells, which are attached by cotton thread to a spiral armature formed of a plant fiber. The armature has been wound round with cotton thread and the spiral coils secured to each other by turns of the thread. Round the middle and at each end is a band of red plush sewn over a fibrous material. "*Benin.* Gauntlet of rare type formed of cowrie shells and 3 bands of red cloth. From the collection of the late William Pilkington of Erdington, Birmingham, sold at Glendinings. 24 June 1929" (Fuller).

BEADS

Representations of beads occur on a wide variety of forms. They represent mainly coral and agate. Coral beads form the collar or choker worn by the king, also the cap and the wings to this cap (e.g., 124, Plate XXV). The king, at certain ceremonies, also wears a shirt of coral beads (e.g., 101, Plate XIX). Cylindrical coral beads are worn as a band round the forehead (e.g., 239, Plate XXII). At the center of this band, and on each side, can be seen a cylindrical bead, probably in real life of agate. Clusters of oval coral beads appear on caps (e.g., 239 and 124). An oval coral bead is sometimes worn above the forehead (e.g., 121). A variety of bead strands hanging from a cap are well represented on memorial heads. Strands of beads are worn across the chest from one shoulder to the side. When a figure is wearing such strands, but from each shoulder so that they cross on the chest and around the back, then the representation is of a king (e.g., 103, Plate XXIV).

"Great Benin. Six coral and 4 agate beads. Originally in the Bankfield Museum, Halifax. Obtained through the Hon. curator, H. Ling Roth, who fig[d] them in his 'Great Benin,' p. 19, fig. 9, types 2, 3, and 6. (See also figs. 10, 11, and 12 pp. 25–27, Pitt-Rivers' 'Antique Works of Art from Benin,' figs. 121, 227, 228, and 229. 24 July 1920" (Fuller).

35. Bead. *Agate.* L. 1⅜″. Diam. ⅜″. *Fuller.* B.0/5.
Cylindrical. The diameter of the hole through the bead is .3 cms.

36. Bead. *Agate.* L. 1⅝″. Diam. ½″. *Fuller.* R.2/45.
Cylindrical.

37. Bead. *Agate.* L. 1⅝″. Diam. ½″. *Fuller.* R.2/46
Cylindrical.

38. Bead. *Agate.* L. 1⅝″. Diam. ⅜. *Fuller.* B.5/62.
Cylindrical.

39. Bead. *Coral.* L. 1¼″. *Fuller.* B.5/65.
Oval. The diameter of the hole is .3 cms.

40. Bead. *Coral.* L. 1⅛″. *Fuller.* B.5/43.
Oval.

41. Bead. *Coral.* L. 1″. *Fuller.* B.1/79.
Oval.

42. Bead. *Coral.* Diam. ⅜″. *Fuller.* B.1/61.
Round. Diameter of hole. 1 cm.

43. Bead. *Coral.* Diam. ⅜″. *Fuller.* 7/40.
Round. Diameter of hole. ⅜″.

44. Bead. *Coral.* Diam. ⅜″. *Fuller.* 7/35.
Round. Diameter of hole ⅜″.

BOXES

The more common form of box carved by the Edo is what is usually termed a kola-nut box. It was used to hold kola nuts and other offerings, such as food. A chief would carry offerings in a box to the king.

45. Box. *Wood, Brass* (Beaten), *Coconut.* L. 22″. Ht. 6⅝″. *CNHM* 91249, 1–2.
Plate XLIV
An oblong kola-nut box, the lid of which is carved with two heads facing each other, in the style of the large wooden memorial head (129, Plate XXXIX), save that the headdress has wings, one on each side, similar to the wings to the memorial heads 125 and 124 (Plate XXXV). The choker, the two wings, and the top of both heads are covered with beaten brass which is riveted to the wood. The supra-orbital marks and the pupils of the eyes are inlaid with coconut.

46. Box. *Wood.* L. 23⅜″. W. 8″. Ht. 5½″. *CNHM* 89691.
The top, sides, and ends of this kola-nut box are decorated with guilloche designs in low relief with small bosses in the loops. This piece is similar to that in Roth, 1903: Fig. 117, of the Liverpool Museum.

47. Box. *Wood.* L. 19¾″. W. 3½″. Ht. 6¼″. *CNHM* 91250, 1 and 2.
Plate XX
The top, sides, and ends of this kola-nut box are carved in low relief with animal forms and geometric designs. In each of two of the four panels of the lid are two snakes, one biting the tail of the other. On one side of the box the three main areas are separated by a leopard. At each end is a fishlike form with a head resembling somewhat that of a deer without horns—perhaps, the head of a cow.

48. Box. *Wood, Brass* (Beaten). Diam. 15¾". *CNHM* 89830, 1–2.

Plate XXIII

A circular box ornamented with narrow bands of beaten brass on which are various motifs, including guilloches, scales, triangles, round discs, and half-moons. Similar to that illustrated in Roth, 1903: Figs. 115–16, of the British Museum.

49. Box. *Wood.* L. 7". W. 5½". Ht. 4½". *Fuller.* R.1/67.

Kola-nut box in the form of the head of a leopard, decorated with circular spots. "*Great Benin.* Leopard's head Box. Collected by Dr. J. G. Whittendale, late of Lime House, Bishop's Waltham. (see Webster's Catalogue: No. 29 fig. 70). 28 April 1917" (Fuller).

50. Box. *Ivory.* L. 5⅞". W. 5". Ht. 1¾". *Fuller.* R.2/27.

A kola-nut box in the shape of a mud fish with its tail in its mouth (cf. similar piece in Pitt-Rivers (1900: Pl. XLVII, Figs. 372, 373).

51. Casket. *Brass.* L. 7¼". W. 5½". Ht. 4½". *Fuller.* R.2/24.

A small brass casket from which the lid is missing. A better example is in the Liverpool Museum, and an elaborate casket of related type, the lid of which represent the roof of the Palace at Benin, is in Berlin (*vide* Von Luschan, 1919: T.90).

52. Lid. *Bronze.* L. 4⅛". W. 1⅞". *CNHM* 89778.

Lid of a brass box decorated in low relief with the figure of a chief holding an *ebē,* in his right hand; cicatrization marks are chased on his body.

BRACELETS

Bracelets are usually made of ivory, cast bronze or brass, iron, or brass cast on iron. Some bracelets are made of brass with settings for coral, e.g., 73, as are hair ornaments.

A variety of forms are used as decoration: human heads, animal heads, and figures, cowrie shells, objects used as medicine, and geometric forms.

Not infrequently in collections one finds bracelets not of Edo manufacture but which are trade items from the north.

The figures on plaques 257 and on 261 are shown wearing bracelets.

53. Bracelet. *Bronze* Max. Diam. 4⅞". Thickness 1". *Fuller.* R.3/12.

Plate XXXVI

Cast bronze bracelet with heads of four horses in low relief (cf. horses' heads with the pendant plaque of a European horseman, 283). This bracelet may have been a pair with a similar armlet in the Pitt-Rivers Museum, Oxford, No. B.II.32, which was collected in 1909 by N. W. Thomas and said to be used in war or worship of Osun. "*Great Benin.* Fine bronze armlet of unusual type representing 4 horses–heads in high relief. Originally in the Bankfield Museum, Halifax, and figured in 'Great Benin' by H. Ling Roth, p. 16, fig. 49. 24. July, 1920" (Fuller).

54. Bracelet. *Bronze.* Max. Diam. 3⅞". *Fuller.* R.3/8.

Decorated with two mud fish and two heads of leopards in low relief. A pair with 55(?).

55. Bracelet. *Bronze.* Max. Diam. 4⅛". *Fuller.* R.3/9.

As 54.

56. Bracelet. *Bronze.* Max. Diam. 3¾". *Fuller.* R.3/10.

Decorated with two rosettes, similar to those in the corners of plaques, and two double mud fish in low relief.

57. Bracelet. *Ivory.* Max. Diam. 4". *Fuller.* R.3/1.

Decorated, in low relief, with four heads of leopards, cowrie shells, and guilloche motifs. "*Great Benin.* Ivory armlet with cowrie shell, etc., design. Originally in the Bankfield Museum, Halifax, and obtained through H. Ling Roth, the Hon. Curator and author of 'Great Benin' (see 2 specimens in B.M; Pitt-Rivers' 'Antique Works etc.' fig. 170). 24 July, 1920" (Fuller).

58. BRACELET. *Brass.* Max. Diam. 2⅞". *Fuller.* R.3/5.

*

Decorated, in low relief, with a continuous series of forms representing cowrie shells. "*Benin.* One of 4 bangles from the collection of Ralph Locke one of the two survivors of the Massacre on 4 January 1897 which led to the punitive expedition. 4 March 1930" (Fuller).

59. BRACELET. *Brass.* Max. Diam. 2⅞". *Fuller.* R.3/2.

*

Decorated, in low relief with three motifs, each with three twisted elements. "*Benin.* One of 4 bangles from the collection of Ralph Locke, one of the two survivors of the Massacre on 4 January 1897 which led to the punitive expedition. 4 March 1930" (Fuller).

60. BRACELET. *Brass.* Max. Diam. 3" *Fuller.* R.3/4.

*

Similar to 59. "*Benin.* One of 4 bangles from the collection of Ralph Locke one of the two survivors of the Massacre on 4 January 1897 which led to the punitive expedition. 4 March 1930" (Fuller).

61. BRACELET. *Brass.* Max. Diam. 2¾". *Fuller.* R.3/3.

*

Plain. "*Benin.* One of 4 bangles from the collection of Ralph Locke, one of the two survivors of the Massacre on 4 January 1897 which led to the punitive expedition. 4 March 1930" (Fuller).

62. BRACELET. *Bronze.* Max. Diam. 4". Thickness 1½". *Fuller.* R.3/34.
A heavy cast bracelet decorated in low relief by a series of forms giving an appearance to the whole of being twisted. The form is not a complete circle; each end forms a flattened surface which is chased. "*Benin.* A pair of bronze armlets of early type worn only by wives of nobility. Collected by Ralph Locke, one of the two survivors of the Benin Massacre which led to the Punitive expedition of 1897 under Admiral Sir Harry H. Rawson. 15 June, 1937" (Fuller).

63. BRACELET. *Bronze.* Max. Diam. 3¾". Thickness 1⅜". *Fuller* R.3/32.
Similar to 62.

64. BRACELET. *Bronze.* Max. Diam. 3¼". Thickness ¾". *Fuller.* R.2/44.
Cast bracelet decorated with four human Negro heads in relief. "*Benin.* 25 May, 1927" (Fuller).

65. BRACELET. *Iron, Brass.* Max. Diam. 4⅜". CNHM 91267.
Iron bracelet with three heads of brass cast on the iron band.

66. BRACELET. *Iron.* Max. Diam. 1 13/16". *Fuller.* B.O/62.

*

"Benin. 20 April 1926" (Fuller).

67. BRACELET. *Iron, Brass.* Diam. 3". CNHM 89808.

*

Similar to 65.

68. BRACELET. *Brass.* Diam. 3½". CNHM 91266.
Cast brass bracelet with, in low relief, four African heads, very similar in form to those of ornamental masks, alternating with four shapes representing screw heads. The bracelet has been broken on one side and mended by recasting. A pair with 69.

69. BRACELET. *Brass.* Diam. 3⅜". CNHM 89807.
Not mended as 68, with which it forms a pair.

70. BRACELET. *Brass.* Max. Diam. 3½". *Fuller.* R.3/6.
Cast brass bracelet formed of a circular band, incised, with four angular projecting ornaments giving an appearance that the object is square in shape. "Benin. 20 April 1926" (Fuller).

71. BRACELET. *Brass.* Max. Diam. 3⅜". *Fuller.* R.3/7.

Similar to 70 except that the band is not incised. "Benin. 20 April 1926" (Fuller).

72. BRACELET. *Brass.* Max. Diam. 3". *CNHM* 89805.

*

Similar to 70.

73. BRACELET. *Brass, Coral.* Diam. 2⅞". *CNHM* 89809.

*

This bracelet of cast brass has six oblong settings in relief for pieces of coral. (Refer "Hair Ornaments.")

74. BRACELET. *Brass.* Diam. 3½". *CNHM* 89806.

*

Decorated with projections, oblong and circular in shape, which are covered with punch marks.

75. BRACELET. *Ivory.* Max. Diam. 2¾". *Fuller.* R.3/11.

No decoration.

COCKS

Bronze cocks are used to decorate the shrines of queen-mothers. "In some households, particularly those of people of high rank, there is an altar to the mothers of the living and past household heads, decorated with *uxurhe* (rattles) and wooden images of fowls" (Bradbury, 1957). Some carved wooden cocks are covered with beaten brass, e.g., 82.

76. COCK. *Bronze.* Ht. 20". *Fuller.* R.2/10.
Plate X
A very fine example of a bronze cock. The sides of the base are decorated, in low relief, with a looped-strap motif with a small boss in each loop. On the stand, between the cock's feet, is, in low relief, an elephant's head and trunk, which ends in a human hand holding a trefoil. The armatures for the legs of the cock are iron rods. "*Benin.* See Sotheby's Catalogue, 18 October 1949, Lot 247, for a similar bronze cock, but not so fine, which went to Burney for Murray of the Nigerian Museums. . . . This specimen of mine is referred to in the catalogue" (Fuller).

77. COCK. *Bronze.* Ht. 3½". L. 5¼". *Fuller.* R.1/66.
Whereas 76 may have been made in the eighteenth century, this small cock would appear to be of relatively recent workmanship. "*Benin.* Bronze fowl (see Pitt-Rivers' 'Works of Art from Benin,' Figs. 301, 348). 7 June, 1919" (Fuller).

78. COCK. *Brass.* Ht. 5⅛". L. 5¾". *CNHM* 89791.
Rather crude casting, very "brassy," with a high green patina.

79. COCK. *Brass.* Ht. 5⅞". L. 4¾". *CNHM* 89792.
Similar to 78.

80. COCK. *Wood.* Ht. 5¼". L. 8½". *Fuller.* R.1/63.
A fine piece of low-relief carving, probably fairly recent. The eyes are inlaid with coconut. Probably a pair with 81. "*Benin,* Wood cock collected by Dr. J. G. Whittendale late of Lime House, Bishop's Waltham. 28 April, 1917" (Fuller).

81. COCK. *Wood.* Ht. 5¼". L. 8¾" *Fuller.* R.1/64.
Probably a pair with 80. "*Benin.* Collected by Dr. J. G. Whittendale late of Lime House, Bishop's Waltham. 28 April 1917" (Fuller).

82. COCK. *Wood, Brass* (Beaten). Ht. 17¼". *CNHM* 91261.
"Carved cock, partly covered with beaten brass. Similar to that figure in Webster Catalogue, Vol. III, No. 18, fig. 65 but without knob on top; in this speciment it has apparently been sawed off" (*CNHM* Catalogue). Around the side of the circular base is a guilloche in low relief, which is covered with beaten brass.

83. COCK. *Wood.* Ht. 10¼". Diam. of base 5⅞". *Fuller.* R.1/65.
Plate XLII
Carved cock, standing on a round base

and having a spike sticking up from its back, all carved from one piece of wood. "*Benin*. Wooden fowl of conventional type being a stand for a small ivory tusk and probably used on an altar. Of smaller size than usual (see Pitt-Rivers, p. 84, pl. 42, fig. 320–1). From the collection of the late William Pilkington of Erdington, Birmingham, sold at Glendinings. 24 June, 1929" (Fuller).

84. Cock. *Wood*. Ht. 11¼″. Diam. of base 7¾″. *CNHM* 209095.

FANS

As mentioned in the introductory essay, fans are made of cowskin and buckskin decorated with red-cloth shapes and fine stitching of antelope skin, the stitching alone sometimes forming the decorative elements. Fans are made in the leatherworker's ward.

85. Fan. *Hide, Wood, Flannel*, L. 15″. Max. W. 9⅝″. *Fuller*. R.2/47.
One side appears to be polished, and on this side are appliquéd designs in red flannel, stitched with hide. The handle is of wood covered with leather and to it is attached a thong to go round the wrist.

86. Fan. *Hide, Wood, Flannel*. L. 12¾″. Max. W. 7½″. *Fuller*. R.2/50.
Similar to 85, though the appliquéd work is less elaborate and the skin is unpolished, the natural animal hair having been left.

87. Fan. *Hide, Wood, Flannel*. L. 12½″. Max. W. 7⅛″. *Fuller*. R.2/49.
Similar to 86.

88. Fan. *Hide, Wood*. L. 15⅛″. Max. W. 10¼″. *Fuller*. R. 2/53.
Similar to 86, except the designs are formed of hide and not flannel.

89. Fan. *Hide, Wood, Flannel*. L. 16¾″. Max. W. 10½″. *Fuller*. R.2/56.
Very similar to 86, with the same designs.

90. Fan. *Hide, Wood, Flannel*. L. 18¼″. Max. W. 12¼″. *Fuller*. R.2/55.
Similar to 86, though the designs are more elaborate.

91. Fan. *Hide, Wood*. L. 19¾″. Max. W. 13⅝″. *Fuller*. R.2/54.
Similar to 88.

92. Fan. *Hide, Wood, Flannel*. L. 21⅞″. Max. W. 15¾″. *Fuller*. R.2/52.
Plate II
A fine piece, similar to 85 but with more elaborate designs in red flannel covering the surface, including a representation of the elephant.

93. Fan. *Hide, Wood, Flannel*. L. 21¼″. Max. W. 14″. *Fuller*. R.2/51.
Plate II
A fine piece with an over-all design more abstract than those on R.2/52. "*Benin*. Collection of Ralph Locke one of the two survivors of the Massacre of 4 January 1897. 4 March 1930" (Fuller).

94. Fan. *Brass* (Beaten). L. 11¾″. Max. W. 7¼″. *Fuller*. R.2/48.
The body of the fan has designs on it, including the representation of a blacksmith's hammer and a sword (*ada*), made by punch marks which closely resemble the stitching used on the hide fans. The handle is attached by copper rivets, following the pattern of stitches of a hide fan.

FIGURES FROM STANDS

In a number of collections of Benin art small bronze figures in the round are often to be encountered. They frequently show a break around a basal piece upon which the figure stands or are broken off above the ankles. Most of these figures originate from groupings of figures cast on a rectangular stand. This stand was placed on an altar. The figures are assembled along the sides and back of the stand, which is open in an area in the middle. Into this area offerings of kola nuts would be placed.

Notable examples of these rectangular stands or altar pieces are in the Staatliches Völkerkunde Museum, Munich (No. ii.2?), and the Royal Scottish Museum, Edinburgh (No. 98.380). The figures found on these two stands are such as are included under this heading. Generally, there are three female figures at the back of the stand; in the center, a queen-mother figure with a conical hat, flanked on either side by a female attendant (as 99), holding up a square, flat object similar to that held by the female figure of pendant plaque 288 (Plate XXX). In front of each female attendant would be figures, such as 98 (Plate XX), holding a shield and spears, and in front of them two figures similar to 95 (Plate XX). Again, in front of these two would be two leopards, as 100. The base of the altarpiece might stand some 3 inches high, and along the front edge would be a frieze of emblems related to sacrifice, such as the skull of a cow and leopard, emblems some of which are to be found round the flanged bases of memorial heads (e.g., 131 and 122).

These altarpieces appear to be related mainly to the queen-mother, whose position at the center on the back is prominent. The leopard is a symbol of the king. Somewhat similar altarpieces appear on the present King of Benin's shrines to his ancestors, though with the king prominent and central, and lacking female figurines. These modern altarpieces recall older and larger ones, notably the two in the Museum für Völkerkunde, Berlin-Dahlem (III C. 8164 and 5, illustrated in Von Luschan, 1919: Tables 79, 80, and 81).

95. FIGURE. *Bronze.* Ht. 4¾". *Fuller. R. 2/33.*
Plate XX
Cast bronze figure holding a blacksmith's hammer in his left hand and part of a staff in his right. He has a cross on his chest. His "bowler hat" is similar to that worn by the figure of plaque 262. This piece is similar to 96. It recalls the two similar figures on the front of the stand (ii.2?) in Munich and the stand 98.380 in Edinburgh. The specimen shows clearly the elaborate projection of the kilt upward on the left side, an item of costume of some dignitaries and noticeable in the plaques. "*Benin.* Bronze figure portion of a group of figures. 11 February, 1913" (Fuller).

96. FIGURE. *Bronze.* Ht. 5½". *CNHM 89789.*
Plate XX
Similar to 95, but not such a good casting and differing particularly with respect to three "whiskers" on the cheeks, running from each corner of the mouth.

97. FIGURE. *Bronze.* Ht. 7⅞". *CNHM 89786.*
Plate XX
Similar to 96, though a rougher casting. This piece shows part of the stand from which it was broken. A snake twines round on the left side and behind the figure.

98. FIGURE. *Bronze.* Ht. 8⅛". *CNHM 89787.*
Plate XX
Figure with a headdress in the shape of a miter, wearing a coral-bead shirt, a necklace of leopard's teeth, and a bell suspended on his chest. At the back of the figure a long tassel hangs down from the collar, a feature to be observed on 102 (Plate XLV). In his left hand is the top

half of a shaft, perhaps a spear. His right hand is missing and also his feet. (Refer Munich and Edinburgh as under 95 above.)

99. Figure. *Bronze.* Ht. 7″. *CNHM* 89788.

Figure of a woman with a high narrow headdress and showing cicatrization marks on her body. The left hand is broken off. (Refer Munich and Edinburgh as under 95 above.)

100. Leopard. *Bronze.* Ht. 2⅛″. L. 5⅛″. *CNHM* 89790.

Cast figure of a leopard with a collar round its neck. (Refer Munich and Edinburgh as under 95 above.)

FIGURES IN THE ROUND

101. Figure. *Bronze.* Ht. 10½″. *Fuller.* R.3/36.
Plate XIX

Figure cast on a brass rod which has been broken off from what may well have been a further piece of a short staff, as it recalls a smilar piece in Lagos. The figure wears a coral-bead shirt and cap, which has wings to it, as 124 (Plate XXXV), and his left hand is shown with the palm turned down, as in the position of the figure of the king in 104. However, he does not have strands of beads passing from each shoulder across his chest and around the waist, a feature generally indicative of a king. Instead, he has a large agate bead suspended from a single-stranded coral necklace upon his chest (cf. kilt and projection with those on 102).

"*Great Benin.* Bronze Figure. The face appears to be of brass. Collected by Dr. J. G. Whittendale, late of Lime House, Bishop's Waltham (see Webster's Catalogue No. 29, fig 141). 28 April, 1917" (Fuller).

102. Figure. *Bronze.* Ht. 15⅛″. *Fuller.* R.2/22.
Plate XLV

Fine casting of a chief, which has unfortunately been buckled. In his right hand he probably held an *ebẽ*. The manner in which a soldier's sword was worn, stuck out behind horizontally to the ground, is clearly shown, a feature not ascertainable from the depiction of such weapons on the plaques. The method by which a leopard-tooth collar acted as a means of suspending a bell on the chest and a tassel down the back is also clearly shown on this figure. (Refer to Forman, W. and B., and Dark, 1960: Plate 15, p. 34.) "*Benin.* See for a Similar specimen:—Websters' Cat. 21, fig. 124" (Fuller).

103. Figure. *Bronze.* Ht. 26¾″. *CNHM* 8260.
Plate XXIV

Very heavy figure—a solid casting—of a king with a loop from the head. In his right hand he holds an *ebẽ*, which has on it, in low relief, four smaller ones, on both the front and the back. From the right shoulder to the *ebẽ* is a support, which undoubtedly acted as a gate in the pouring system when casting was taking place. A similar support runs from the left shoulder to the back of the scepter or gong, which is held in the left hand. At some time the handle of the *ebẽ* held in the right hand must have been broken off and been replaced by a poorly cast one. The protuberances forward on each side of the cheeks, which, with the wings to the cap, are a feature of memorial heads of the post 1820's (cf. 124 and 125), are bent down on each side of the head; this may have occurred when casting. The same characteristic is present in 104. On the scepter, gong, or medicine horn or staff (cf. Roth, 1903: Figs. 61–65, 226, and 260–61), held in the right hand, is a figure in relief holding in its left hand a staff bent over at the top, like a blacksmith's hammer, and in its right a staff.

This large bronze figure is shown wearing a coral-bead collar with an extension back and front, like a bib, over his coral-bead shirt. Across his chest is a band of coral beads to which is attached a large oval coral bead and, below it, a small celt (cf. 156).

The figure is cast on a rod, which

would appear to be of brass and which acts as an armature. The loop recalls the handles of *ebē*. The figure is illustrated in Roth, 1903: Figs. 70*a* and 71.

104. FIGURE. *Bronze.* Ht. 27″. *CNHM* 8261.
This figure of a king with a large loop extending from the top of his head is similar to that in the British Museum (97-550. Cockburn), illustrated in Forman, W. and B., and Dark, 1960: Plates 60–62, and comparable to the larger one, 103. It differs, however, from this latter in that the left arm is held forward and horizontal with the ground, the palm of the hand down and the fingers curved downward, as with 101. In his right hand are the remains of what was probably an *ebē*.

105. FIGURE. *Ivory.* Ht. 15½″. *Fuller.* R.3/35.
Plate XII
This fine ivory figure of a king seated on a throne is well worn in the front; at the back, however, the carving is clear and precise. Unfortunately, the forearms are missing. The throne recalls a round stool carved from a single block of wood, which is associated with the arm and hand. The arm and hand are worshiped by people. It is represented, sometimes by an anklet of cowries, which is worshiped (see Melzian, 1937: pp. 90, 214). Just under the rim of the stool is a band of forms in low relief which appear to represent cowrie shells. A similar band is near the base of the stool.
"*Benin.* Old and much weathered ivory figure of a man (? one of the Kings). This stood on a post close to and in front of the King's house. It was collected by Dr. Felix Norman Roth in 1897 when medical officer to the expedition to Benin City and remained on clearing up after the forces had left. [The figure was] acquired from his widow, Mrs. Winifred N-R. through H. Ling Roth [in] whose 'Great Benin' 1903, [see] p. 201, figs. 210 for a plate of this specimen. 17 May 1923, Fuller Collection. Deposited on loan at B.M." (Fuller).

"?*Benin.* These three little nut carvings were attached when I purchased the figure but doubtless have no connection with it. They were collected by Dr. Felix Norman Roth in 1897 during the Benin Expedition but need not necessarily come from that city. 17 May 1923" (Fuller).

106. FIGURE. *Wood.* Ht. 19¼″. *CNHM* 209655.
*
Figure of a woman, carved in ebony, sitting on a seat. The figure is very narrow. Collected by Hambly and probably carved just before his visit to Benin.

107. FIGURE. *Wood.* Ht. 18⅛″. *CNHM* 209656.
*
Figure of a woman, carved in ebony, kneeling on the right knee. Collected by Hambly and probably carved just before his visit.

HAIR ORNAMENTS

Ornaments for the hair were cast of brass in a variety of shapes into which were set, in a special form of beeswax, pieces of coral. The king supplied the coral to the brassworkers. Hair ornaments were mainly either of a form which had a long pin for sticking into the hair or like a finger ring which was tied in the hair. They were worn by the king's wives and nobility.

108. HAIR ORNAMENT. *Brass, Coral.* L. 2⅞″. Ht. 1⅞″. *Fuller.* R.3/26.
"*Benin.* Old cast brass ring inlaid with carnelian. From the collection of Lady Gantly sold at Sotheby's. 15 July, 1924, lot 199 (see H. L. Roth's 'Great Benin' 1903, Fig. 32, Webster's Cat: No. 21, figs. 57 & 60. 16 August 1924" (Fuller).

109. HAIR ORNAMENT. *Brass.* L. 6¼″. Max. Diam. 1″. *Fuller.* R.3/23.
"*Benin.* Old cast brass ring originally in-

laid with carnelian. From the collection of Lady Gantly, sold at Sotheby: 15 July, 1924, lot 199 (see H. Ling Roth's "Great Benin" 1903, fig. 32; Webster's Catalogue No. 21, figs. 57 & 60). 16 August, 1924" (Fuller).

110. HAIR ORNAMENT. *Brass.* L. 6½".
   CNHM 89811.
      *
Consisting of a pin with a long horizontal bar into the top of which coral was inlaid. Only the setting material, however, remains.

111. HAIR ORNAMENT. *Brass.* L. 10¼".
   CNHM 89814.
      *
Like 110.

112. HAIR ORNAMENT. *Brass.* L. 8¾".
   CNHM 89813.
      *
Like 110.

113. HAIR ORNAMENT. *Brass, Coral.* L. 3⅝". *CNHM* 89817.
"Hairpin. Slender pointed stem merging into 3 (one broken off) cylindrical shaped projections. Coral beads inserted in ends" (CNHM catalogue).

114. HAIR ORNAMENT. *Brass, Coral.* L. 7⅛". *CNHM* 89812.
Like 110, except pieces of the coral inlay are still present.

115. HAIR ORNAMENT. *Brass, Coral.* L. 8⅝". *CNHM* 89815.
"Brass Hairpin. Horizontal bar. Oblong ends. 3 cylindrical projections with coral beads inserted in ends. Upper side of bar formerly inlaid. Broken pin midway of bar" (CNHM catalogue).

116. HAIR ORNAMENT. *Brass.* L. 8⅞".
   CNHM 91275.
Some setting remains in the top of the bars which form this pin.

HEADS

When a king succeeded to the throne on the demise of his predecessor, he would order an altar to be set up where he would worship the deceased ancestor. For this altar, objects were cast and carved, including bronze heads in memory of the deceased. On these heads were placed carved tusks which leaned against the wall at the back of the altar. "In the king's compound, on a raised platform, running the whole breadth of each, beautiful idols were found. All of them were caked over with human blood, and by giving them a slight tap, crusts of blood would, as it were, fly off. Lying about were big bronze heads, dozens in a row, with holes at the top, into which immense carved ivory tusks were fixed" (Dr. Felix Roth *in* Roth, 1903: x). The medallion-like centerpiece of one side joining two of the legs of the carved wooden stool 303 (Plate XIV) depicts, with other forms, a head with a tusk resting on it. However, some heads, those considered early, in all probability did not support such tusks (e.g., 117, Plate VI, and 118, Plate XXVII, and the St. Louis head). The number of heads made at any one time is not known. A considerable number of them survive to us. They come from the compounds where the Oba of Benin used to have shrines to all past ancestors.

Heads of brass were also cast for past queen-mothers (e.g., 130, Plate XXV). Chiefs had heads carved of wood which were often covered with beaten brass (e.g., 129, Plate XXXIX).

Changes in style and technical mastery of *cire-perdue* casting of memorial heads have been given considerable attention by scholars. It is generally assumed that the earliest heads are those which are cast very thin, using little metal—a feature of remarkable technical control—and which are most naturalistic in appearance. The main reason for this assumption is that the Edo learned the art of casting bronze from Ife, and, as the bronze antiquities from Ife surviving to us show remarkable naturalistic features, then the earliest Benin heads would be those which most closely resemble heads found at Ife. We do not yet know when the fine Ife bronze work was made, but the reign of Oguola, in whose time the art of casting was learned at Benin, certainly took place before the advent of the Portuguese in 1485. The reader is referred to Elisofon and Fagg, 1958, Forman, W. and B., and Dark, 1960, and Underwood, 1949, for further information on this topic. The probable sequence of the bronze heads in this exhibition, from the earliest to the last century, is indicated by the order 117 through 125.

117. HEAD. *Bronze.* Ht. 7¾″. W. 6⅝″. Diam. of base 5⅝″. *Fuller.* R.2/20.
Plate VI
This fine casting of what is generally considered an early example of the Benin brassworkers' art was cast to a thinness varying from 2 to 3 mm. The head weighs only 3.9 lbs. On the inside is a circular stamp mark which reads: "Douane Française." The surface has a pleasing greenish luster. The hair is indicated by chased circles with stippling marks between them. Two strips at the center of the forehead are of iron, as are also the pupils of the eyes. Above and behind each ear are three protuberances which suggest that three plaits of hair, in relief, ran down each side of the head to the level of the ear hole, but have broken off.
From *Traditional Art of the British*

Colonies: An Exhibition Held at the RAI, June 21–July 20, 1949, pp. 4–5, Item 21: *"Human Head in bronze with unusual features:* The early date of this unique piece is indicated by the thinness and light weight of the casting as well as by the tribal marks on the forehead; it is probably early 16th century. It has been suggested that it represents the pathological condition of acromegaly, and representations of deformed persons were not uncommon at Benin" (Wm. Fagg).

Fuller: "Unique head . . . the supposed Seattle specimen in Elisofon's '*The Sculpture of Africa*' fig. 165, p. 255, is an extraordinary error for this head." The head is also illustrated in Von Luschan, 1917, I/Abb. 529 and was reproduced in Dr. Ansorge's 1909 Auction Catalogue.

"*Benin.* 'Ancient and unique Bronze Head described by Wm. Fagg of the B.M. as a memorial Head, seems to belong to the earliest period at Benin from which examples survive (probably the 15th century), but it is not typical, apparently representing a pathological condition such as acromegaly. See E. Elisofon and W. Fagg "*The Sculpture of Africa,*" 1958, fig. 165 where this specimen is . . . attributed to the Eugene Fuller collection in the Seattle Art Museum; Seattle (p. 255)!! I have exhibited it many times, once in New York, many years ago" (Fuller). Reference is to an exhibition at the Museum of Modern Art in 1935 (see Sweeney, 1935, Plate 259).

118. HEAD. *Bronze.* Ht. 8⅛″. City Art Museum, St. Louis No. 1296.
Plate XXVIII
An example of an early head. The two forehead strips were of iron; the pupils are of iron. Cf. similar heads in, e.g., the University Museum, Philadelphia, in Lagos and in the British Museum (illustrated in Forman, W. and B., and Dark, 1960: Plates 63, 64). This head is illustrated in *The Negro in Art* by Alain Locke, 1940: 213, and in *Cahiers d'art,* 1932, No. 3:216.

119. HEAD. *Bronze.* Ht. 10¾″. *Fuller.* R.2/23.

This head has a high collar of twenty-three rings. On the left side of the coral-bead cap are two clusters of coral beads, on the right is one such cluster. The pupils, which are large, are of iron. Above each eye are three keloids. The casting is lighter and perhaps earlier than a similar head 120. It is a more recent casting than the St. Louis head. *"Benin. Bronze head of ordinary type but old and fine. 23 October 1906"* (Fuller).

120. HEAD. *Bronze.* Ht. 12½″. *CNHM* 8146.
Plate XXXI
This head, which has a collar of nineteen rings, is a light reddish-brown in color. It is similar to 119, though the pupils are noticeably smaller.

121. HEAD. *Bronze.* Ht. 12⅛″. *CNHM* 8265.
This head has a flanged base, two coral clusters on both sides of the coral-bead cap, and two strips of iron on the forehead. The pupils are of iron. Below each eye are eight chased circles; above are three keloids. The casting is light brown in color with a greenish patina. Around the flanged base, in relief and on a relief guilloche, are a number of forms: from the front and moving round the base to the right are a cow head, celt, and elephant head and trunk ending in a human hand holding a trefoil, mud fish, a skull (of a bird, or a leopard), mud fish, celt, cow head, celt, mud fish, the skull form again, mud fish, the elephant-head motif again, and a celt. The casting shows a fine precision in detail but is probably more recent than 120.

122. HEAD. *Bronze.* Ht. 12⅝″. *CNHM* 8264.
Plates VIII, IX
Similar to 121. Around the flanged base in relief, on a low-relief looped-strap motif, are, reading from the front around to the right, a celt, an elephant head with the trunk ending in a human hand, holding a trefoil but double in form, standing leopard with its tail curved over its back,

a cow head, celt, cow head, the leopard form again, and the elephant motif again.

123. HEAD. *Bronze.* Ht. 12¼″. *CNHM* 8148.
Similar to 122. Around the flanged base in relief, reading from the front around to the right, is a cow's head, celt, an elephant head with a trunk ending in a hand holding a trefoil, a skull form (bird or leopard), mud fish, frog, cow head, the skull form, the elephant-head motif, the skull form, cow head, frog, mud fish, the skull form, the elephant-head motif, and a celt.

124. HEAD. *Bronze.* Ht. 20½″. *CNHM* 8147.
Plate XXXV
One of the largest heads cast, it has a collar of thirty-seven rings. Two large wings to the cap indicate that the head was probably not made before King Osemwede's time, since he is credited with the introduction of the winged cap. He reigned about the 1820's. The pupils of the eyes are of iron; the eyelids are chased as are also the eyebrows, in between the supraorbital keloids.

Around the flanged base, in low relief, is a looped-strap motif; in places the artist appears to have lost the regularity of the motif's intertwining. On this motif are a number of relief forms: from the front moving around to the right are a celt, an elephant head with the trunk ending in a human hand holding a trefoil, a leopard, a cow head, mud fish, leopard, cow head, leopard, mud fish, cow head, leopard, and the elephant-head motif. Round the rope border, which decorates the edge of the flange, are relief knobs representing, probably, screw heads.

125. HEAD. *Bronze.* Ht. 15⅜″. *CNHM* 8263.
A head of similar type to 124, but smaller and not so well cast. Round the flanged base, on a low-relief looped-strap motif, are a number of relief forms: from the front moving around to the right are a celt, an elephant head with a trunk

ending in a human hand holding a trefoil, a leopard, frog, cow head, mud fish,
celt, mud fish, cow head, frog, leopard,
and the elephant-head motif.

126. Head. *Bronze.* Ht. 8⅝″. Diam. of
base 5⅜″. *Fuller.* R.4/9.

Plate XIII

A head with iron pupils and three tribal
marks chased above each eye; at the back
is a rectangular slot with, below it, a
chased St. Andrew's cross. The presence
of this slot and the general appearance of
the head suggest that it belongs to a style
of casting which William Fagg has called
"the Udo style" (*vide* Elisofon and Fagg,
1958; Murray, 1961). "*Benin.* Bronze
Head of uncommon type a peculiarity
of which is the large square hole cut out
of the back. Baron von Hügel acquired
the fellow of this specimen for Cambridge. An inferior example is in Pitt-
Rivers' Collection, 'Antique Works of
Art,' 1900, figs. 149–50. (Following in
pencil) 'Udo-Style, 26ᵐ W. of Benin.' (As
above, in ink) Fuller Collection. Deposited on loan at British Museum 10 December 1907" (Fuller).

127. Head. *Bronze.* Ht. 5¼″. Max Diam.
2½″. *Fuller.* R.2/30.

A human head with tetrapodal support.
A ropelike band extends across the cheeks
and chin from each ear. At the back of
the head, in low relief, is a loop ending
in two spirals similar to that found on
certain pyramidal-shaped bells.

128. Head. *Terracotta.* Ht. 10⅜″. *Fuller.*
R.2/21.

Plate IV

Heads of terracotta were made by the
brass-smiths, but they are relatively rare.
The method of tying the choker, which is
formed of lozenge-shaped beads, is shown
at the back of the head. "*Benin.* Head-
base for any ivory tusk of *earthenware* resembling the bronze heads but the work
is much more carefully executed (*vide*
the beads). This specimen seems to be
unique except for the very small female
head in the Pitt-Rivers' Collection (see

his "Antique Works of Art" No. 365). In
recent years (1936) a number of modern
ones have been made for trade but they
look new and are of very poor workmanship. This specimen came out of a large
collection of Benin objects and was in
pieces when acquired by me. The material is very hard. Fuller Collection. Deposited on Loan at the British Museum,
1905 or 6" (Fuller).

129. Head. *Wood, Brass* (Beaten), *Coconut.* Ht. 21¼″. *CNHM* 89829.

Plate XXXIX

A very large wooden memorial head. The
band around the forehead, the collar, the
feather on the left side of the head and
its extension below, and the base are
covered with beaten brass. A beaten brass
strip runs down the forehead and covers
the nose. Around the base is a guilloche
motif. The eyes and tribal marks above
each eye are inlaid with coconut.

130. Head. *Bronze.* Ht. 16¾″. *CNHM*
8262.

Plate XXV

Queen-mother head with an opening for
supporting a tusk behind the coral-bead
conical cap. To the center of the forehead are two strips of iron. Above each
eye are four supraorbital keloids. Above
each ear, on the forehead band of coral
beads, is a cluster of coral beads similar
to those noted above on other memorial
heads. The flanged base of this head is
decorated with a guilloche design in low
relief.

131. Head. *Bronze.* Ht. 18½″. *CNHM*
8149

Queen-mother head of a similar type to
130 but a more recent casting. The front
of the nose is angled in a more upright
direction than on the other heads.
Whereas 130 had only one cluster of coral
beads each side of the cap, this head has
two such clusters. The flanged base,
which has a rope border, is divided into
twenty panels by two parallel lines in relief. Each panel has in it a spiral in low
relief.

132. HEAD. *Wood.* Ht. 13″. W. of base 5½″. *CNHM 209657.*

*

An ebony head collected by Hambly and probably carved about the time of his visit to Benin.

KEYS

Cyril Punch, who first visited Benin in 1889, is quoted by Roth, 1903: 187: "The stores were locked with native locks, the principle of which was a bolt working through staples. The key was a piece of iron with a piece bent at right angles. The keyhole was at different lengths above the bolt, so that only the key of a right length would reach the bolt. Practically, I do not think the locks were much protection."

133. KEY. *Bronze.* L. of key and chain 15⅛″; of key 7⅜″. *Fuller.* R.2/34.

Plate XXIV

A very fine casting of a key and a chain of fourteen links. At the top of the key is a Janus head of an Oba with an arm going down each side to grasp the tail of a leopard. The leopard is shown devouring a goat. Imitations of the heads of screws decorate the handle around which, where it joins the stem, is a coral-bead collar with, on it in relief, two human and two leopard heads. Above the collar, in relief, are lips and the end of a nose. The stem or body of the key has patterns chased on it. Probably a royal key.

134. KEY. *Bronze.* L. 5⅛″. *Fuller.* R.2/35.

Plate XXIV

The handle is decorated in low relief, with the heads of screws, two human heads, and two rope elements. "Collection of Rev. E. E. Hill of West Malling." (Fuller).

135. KEY. *Bronze.* L. 5⅝″. *CNHM 89810.*

Plate XXIV

KNIVES

136. KNIFE. *Iron.* L. 6⅜″. *Fuller.* R.2/57. A yam knife with a blade of iron. "Benin. An unusual short handled billhook type of knife. For a similar specimen see Pitt-Rivers, P. 36. pl. 18, figs. 108–9. 10 April, 1926" (Fuller).

137. KNIFE. *Iron, Brass.* L. 20½″. *Fuller.* R.2/58.

A yam knife with an iron blade and handle upon which has been cast in brass a clenched hand. This form of hand is to be found at the end of certain staff rattles, *uxurhe*, which are part of the furniture of the ancestor shrines of the king.

138. KNIFE. *Iron, Brass.* L. 12⅜″. *Fuller.* R.2/59.

A yam knife similar to 137. The clenched hand of brass appears to contain lead. "Benin. Small iron knife of billhook type with hilt of a closed hand, rather late period. 16 March, 1948" (Fuller).

139. KNIFE. *Iron, Brass.* L. 14⅝″. *Fuller.* R.2/60.

A yam knife with iron blade and a cast brass handle with a leopard's head at the end. The leopard is one of the regal symbols. "Benin. '28.1.32' Fine specimen of this type of knife. An all iron knife or bill hook(?) The edge on this curves. Has handle terminating in a leopard head" (Fuller).

140. KNIFE. *Iron, Brass.* L. 7½″. *Fuller.* R.2/61.

Plate XVIII

A yam knife with an iron blade and a handle of cast brass, terminating in a Janus head in the style of memorial heads with a high collar and no flanged base (e.g., 119 and 120).

141. KNIFE. *Iron.* L. 7¾″. W. 2⅛″. *CNHM 89821.*

A knife with a slender stem widening into a thin flat blade. The thin stem was mounted into the forked branch of a tree and the tool utilized as a razor, according to Hambly.

LAMPS

Lamps were made of beaten and cast brass and of iron. They generally consisted of two or more arms of cast brass, chased with abstract designs and riveted to a circular beaten-brass pan. The arms curved up to a central point above the pan, crossed, and descended to the farther side. A disk of beaten brass with some design on it is attached to the central point. Attached to this point is, generally, some cast form, which may consist of a human figure or be abstract.

Cyril Punch is quoted by Roth (1903: 121), "All the gentry had these lamps. Palm oil was put in the pan, and a piece of raw cotton wool placed on the edge of the pan served as a wick; a small flat piece of iron was placed on the top of the wick to prevent the oil all taking fire at once. . . . The open compounds at night, full of people and lit up with these lamps, were very striking."

142. LAMP. *Brass.* Diam. 5¾". Ht. 16½". *CNHM* 89822.
Plate XXXIV
The tray of the lamp is of beaten brass. The two supports are of cast brass and chased; where they cross is a beaten-brass disk to which is attached an oblong ornamental shape with spiral forms, three links and a long hook, all cast.

143. LAMP. *Brass.* Diam. 8¾". Ht. 23¼". *CNHM* 89823.
Plate XXXIV
Similar to 142 except that the ornamental shape above the disk is a figure of a naked man with a rather prominent penis.

144. LAMP. *Brass.* Diam. 8⅛". Ht. 17¾". *CNHM* 89824.
*
Similar to 142 but with only two supporting bands.

145. LAMP. *Brass.* Diam. 6½". Ht. 20⅛". *CNHM* 89825.
*
Similar to 142.

146. LAMP. *Brass.* Diam. 14⅜". Ht. 28¾". *CNHM* 89826.
Similar to 142 but with three supporting bands and the figure of a bird, an ibis, with outstretched wings as the ornamental shape above the disk. The chain leading to the hook is composed of forty-two small links.

147. LAMP. *Brass.* Diam. 14⅝". Ht. 31⅛". *CNHM* 89827.
Similar to 146 except the bird's wings are closed and there are only three large links.

148. TRAY. *Brass.* W. 4". *CNHM* 89828.
*
The tray or pan of a lamp which is square in shape with the four corners pinched in.

149. HOOK. *Brass.* L. 10⅞". *CNHM* 89820.
*
A hook of cast brass, with chased ornamentation, for a lamp.

150. LAMP. *Iron.* Ht. 38⅜". *CNHM* 89838.
A lamp in the form of an iron dish set on top of a long iron stem fashioned at the end to a narrow point so that the lamp can be stuck in the ground. Cf. Roth, 1903: Fig. 124.

MEDICINE STAFFS AND CONTAINERS

"Osū is the 'god of medicine,' whose assistance must be sought to ensure the effective use of all 'medicines,' curative or otherwise. It is worshipped especially by the professional 'doctors' (*ewaise*) in Benin City and elsewhere" (Bradbury, 1957: 53).

151. MEDICINE HORN. *Ivory, Bronze.* L. 28⅛". *Fuller.* R.1/60.

Plate XLVII

A beautifully carved medicine horn in the shape of a tusk with, at the broad end, a hollow for medicine which can be closed by a lid on a hinge of cast bronze. On the top of this lid is a leopard in relief. Below him, on either side, in low relief, is a mud fish.

On the body of the horn, from the top down, first is an area in low relief of diamond forms, then a band of rings, below which is an elephant decorated with low-relief diamond forms. The rings end in a foot, which rests on top of the elephant's back. The right-hand tusk of the elephant is missing. His trunk ends in a hand, which has been defaced but from which a feather can be seen protruding. Attention was drawn in the section on heads to the elephant's trunk ending in a human hand as a motif on the flanged bases of certain memorial heads (121, 122, 123, 124, 125) and on the base of the bronze cock (76). The elephant is on a stand, the two ends of which are carved in low relief with a snake on one end. Below the stand, on the inner curvature of the tusk, is a knot, which is in full relief, above a small knob. Next, below this, is a hand being eaten by a snake. The body of the snake continues on in a spiral form down the tusk, wrapping itself round another snake, the head of which, however, is pointing down.

On the left and right sides of the elephant, and hence the tusk, is, moving down, a mud fish in full relief caught in a clenched hand. From the hand the arm is represented by a snake in the shape of a spiral with its head pointing down and holding a mud fish in its mouth.

On the outer circumference of the tusk, and below the back of the elephant, is a bird, perhaps an ibis, though the beak is short. The bird has in its mouth a rosette. Below the rosette is the head of a European with a beard, in an old style for this form.

Passing down the stem around which the two snakes intertwine, a crocodile's head is reached, the top of which is on the inner circumference. The crocodile has a mud fish in its mouth. Cf. Roth, 1903: Figs. 209–12.

152. MEDICINE STAFF. *Iron.* L. 26⅜". *CNHM* 89835.

Plate XXIII

Iron staff of three branches on each of which is a chameleon. At the top of the two outer branches is a cluster of six birds, ibis, surrounding a seventh in the center. At the top of the central branch is an ibis on top of a chameleon, surrounded by nine forms of varying shapes, which include an *ada*, a chisel, an *ebē*, spears, and a knife. It seems probable that this is the top only of the staff, a long stem having been broken off.

153. MEDICINE STAFF. *Iron.* L. 49¾". *CNHM* 89836.

Iron staff with, at the top, a cluster of forms similar to those on the central branch of 152, surrounding a chameleon. Below is a chameleon climbing the shaft and below, again, a cluster of five small forms similar to small cone-shaped clapper bells.

154. MEDICINE STAFF. *Iron.* L. 42½". *CNHM* 89837.

Similar to 153 except that the top is missing. Below the top is a leopard. Below, again, are four chameleons. Farther down the shaft is a cluster, similar to 153, with, below it, a chameleon.

155. TUBE. *Bronze.* L. 10½". *CNHM* 89803.

*

Part of a cast bronze tube which may be the basal end of a medicine staff. Cf. Forman, W. and B., and Dark, 1960: Pl. 73.

156. CELT. *Bronze.* L. 1¼". *Fuller.* R.3/24.

A cast bronze celt with chased decoration. A few of these appear in collections, e.g., Manchester. "*Benin.* Model Celt used as a charm. From Dr. W. J. Ansorge's Collection (see 'Man' Vol. III, 1903, No. 102 'Thunderbolt' celts from Benin by Hy Balfour). 30 November 1909" (Fuller).

157. MEDICINE BUNDLE. *Skin.* L. 5¼". W. 4¼". *Fuller.* R.3/31.

*

A small "parcel" of medicine(?) covered with a piece of leopard skin and stitched together around the edges. "Benin Skin Charm. Found in a juju House, Benin City, Punitive Expedition 1897. 19 Dec. 1928" (Fuller).

MESSENGER STAFFS

Staffs or wands, with long handles of cast bronze riveted to a flat blade on which designs are chased, were carried by the Oba's messengers when they were sent to the villages on some task.

158. STAFF. *Bronze.* L. 6¼". CNHM 89819.

*

The portion of a king's messenger's staff representing the bottom of the handle and the top part of the blade. Two figures, in relief and back to back, form the bottom of the handle: one holds a sword across his body with the point down, the other holds a sword in a similar fashion but with the point up. The blade is chased with guilloche designs.

159. STAFF. *Bronze.* L. 17¼". CNHM 91252.

The handle and top part of the blade of a king's messenger's staff. At the top is the figure of a chief holding up an *ebē* in his right hand. Below is another figure of a chief striking an idiophone in the form of an ibis. The handle is riveted with copper rivets to the blade, which is chased with designs.

MUSICAL INSTRUMENTS

The examples of musical instruments represented in the two collections are cast bronze bells, pyramidal and conical in form; a drum; an iron gong and a bronze one; cast bronze idiophones in the form of an ibis; a rattle of ivory and rattles of wood carved in the form of a staff, known as *uxurhe;* and whistles of the side-blast variety cast in bronze and carved in ivory.

The pyramidal bells and *uxurhe* are used in prayer at a shrine. Bradbury (1957: 54) writes that *uxurhe* are placed on ancestor shrines for individual ancestors and on the shrines of the collective ancestors of a group. The *uxurhe* of ordinary folk had a head carved at the top whereas those of the *Oba* usually ended in a hand which sometimes clasped a mud fish. There are examples of royal *uxurhe* in bronze (e.g., 211). The *uxurhe,* when not in use, rests on the shrine, but in prayer, or in cursing, it is banged on the ground for emphasis.

Pyramidal bells are also worn as part of the costume of many dignitaries. Both the figures of plaques 253 and 254 (Plate XXXII), for example, can be seen wearing such a bell on the chest. The designs on the panels of bells vary considerably; both human and animal forms are used as well as geometric motifs. It is possible, as Von Luschan demonstrated, to arrange a number of bells in an order which shows a change from the representation of the European head as the main motif on the front panel to a complete abstraction in which only the long side curls of the hair are the principal form.

According to Chief Ine, the head of the brassworkers in Benin today, who was shown a photograph of bells in the CNHM collection, 195 represents a type made for the king or for the royal family. A bell of the type of 196 and 199 was made for the king's wife.

The figure on plaque 266 (Plate XV) is depicted striking a gong similar to the two examples in the round included here: 201 and 202. The ibis idiophone was played in a similar fashion.

Cast Bronze Bells

160. BELL. *Bronze.* Ht. 11″. Base, L. 5⅞″. W. 5⅝″. *Fuller.* R.1/69.
A pyramidal-shaped bell with, on the front panel, in low relief, an African face surrounded by small spiral, radiating forms. "Rectangular hand bell ornamented has work on 3 sides. One side has Negro head in relief [*sic*] 28.1.32" (Fuller).

161. BELL. *Bronze.* Ht. 7″. Base, L. 3⅞″, W. 4″. *Fuller.* R.1/70.
Plate XXXVII
A very fine pyramidal shaped bell of light casting but with flaring rather than straight sides. This bell is exceptional in that it is gilded. On the front panel, in low relief, in the center, is the bearded face of a European wearing a cap with two feathers in it. The surface of the front panel is chased with figures and heads, which sometimes appear on the kilts of figures on plaques, and with other forms, including a floral guilloche, and the spaces are liberally stippled. The two side panels each have, in low relief at the center, an unbearded European face with a cap without feathers. Similar figures and heads as those on the front panel are chased on these side panels. On the back panel, in low relief, is the figure of a European with a sword in his left hand. The background of this back panel is chased with heads and designs similar to those on the other three panels. This piece, according to Captain Fuller, was brought over by

Captain Lees after the expedition and given to his father. Fuller bought it from Lees.

162. BELL. *Bronze.* Ht. 5⅞″. Base, L. 3¾″, W. 3¾″. *Fuller.* R.1/71.
A pyramidal-shaped bell with flaring rather than straight sides. The front panel contains two mud fish near the top and two near the bottom with, in the center, a Negro head, all in low relief, all cast separately and then laid in the wax model of the bell, which is then cast. The mud fish appear to be of copper. On the two side panels are four mud fish, similarly made and set in the wax, with, at the center, two concentric circles, delineated in relief and filled with stippling marks. The back is plain. The bell has an iron clapper. (Cf. a similar piece in the Musée de Cinquantenaire, Brussels.)

163. BELL. *Bronze.* Ht. 6⅞″. Base, L. 3¾″, W. 3½″. *Fuller.* R.1/72.
A pyramidal-shaped bell with flaring rather than straight sides. On the front panel, in low relief, are four crocodiles with, at the center, a Negro head surrounded by four bosses. Below, between the two lower crocodiles, is a fifth boss. The background is chased with floral guilloche motifs and the empty spaces stippled. The two side panels are similar to the front panel except that there is a sixth boss instead of the head. The back panel is chased all over with a floral guilloche design. The bell has an iron clapper.

164. BELL. *Bronze.* Ht. 6⅝″. Base, L. 3⅜″, W. 3⅜″. *Fuller.* R.1/73.
A pyramidal-shaped bell with flaring rather than straight sides. On the front panel, at the center, is a large spiral, in relief, with, above and below it, a smaller, similar spiral. "*Benin.* Bell w. spiral ornament one side instead of usual face. 18 August 1936" (Fuller).

165. BELL. *Bronze.* Ht. 6⅛″. Base, L. 3⅜″, W. 3 7/16″. *Fuller.* R.1/74.
A pyramidal-shaped bell with straight sides. On the front panel at the center, in relief, is an African head surrounded

by radiating spirals (cf. 160 and 175). Iron clapper. "*Benin.* Bronze bell with curious head on one side (see Webster's Catalogue: 21, Fig. 106). 27 April, 1928" (Fuller).

166. BELL. *Bronze.* Ht. 5⅛". Base, L. 3", W. 2⅝". *Fuller.* R.1/75.

*

A pyramidal-shaped bell with flaring sides, minus its handle. On the front panel, in low relief, is a Negro face. Iron clapper.

167. BELL. *Bronze.* Ht. 6⅛". Base, L. 2⅞", W. 3". *Fuller.* R.1/76.
A pyramidal-shaped bell with slightly flaring sides. On the front panel, which is partially of open-lattice work, in low relief, is an African head surrounded by radiating spirals. Cf. 165. "*Benin.* Bronze bell with iron clapper curiously hung. 11 Feb. 1913" (Fuller).

168. BELL. *Bronze.* Ht. 4⅝". Base, L. 2½", W. 2½". *Fuller.* R.1/77.
A pyramidal-shaped bell. On the front panel, in low relief, is an African face. Iron clapper. "*Benin.* Bronze bell, very old. See wearing of clapper inside. 11 Feb. 1913" (Fuller).

169. BELL. *Bronze.* Ht. 5". Base, L. 2⅜", W. 2⅜". *Fuller.* R.1/78.
A pyramidal-shaped bell. On the front panel, in low relief, are two spirals joined by a loop. Cf. 177. Iron clapper.

170. BELL. *Bronze.* Ht. 5½". Diam. of base 3⅜". *Fuller.* R.1/79.
A round, hourglass-shaped bell chased with various curvilinear and geometric designs. The clapper is of brass and decorated in a manner suggestive of Hausa workmanship. "I know of no other similar specimen Bronze Ceremonial Benin *rattle.* 6 Oct. 1931" (Fuller).

171. BELL. *Bronze.* Ht. 3¾". *CNHM* 89722.
A pyramidal-shaped bell. On the front panel, in low relief, is a form similar to that on 169.

172. BELL. *Bronze.* Ht. 4⅛". *CNHM* 89723.
Similar to 169 but with two looped spirals, one above the other. No clapper.

173. BELL. *Bronze.* Ht. 3⅛". *CNHM* 89724.

*

Similar to 172. The clapper is a cowrie shell.

174. BELL. *Bronze.* Ht. 3⅞". *CNHM* 89734.
Similar to 172, but with only one looped spiral. Iron clapper.

175. BELL. *Bronze.* Ht. 3⅝". *CNHM* 89733.
Close to 171. No Clapper.

176. BELL. *Bronze.* Ht. 3¾". *CNHM* 89729.
Close to 175. Long iron clapper.

177. BELL. *Bronze.* Ht. 4⅛". *CNHM* 89737.
Very similar to 174. Slender iron clapper.

178. BELL. *Bronze.* Ht. 4". *CNHM* 89726.
Similar to 177 except that the looped spirals are developed into the form of a rudimentary European head. Cylindrical clapper.

179. BELL. *Bronze.* Ht. 3¾". *CNHM* 89725.

*

Pyramidal-shaped bell with an African face in low relief at the center of the front panel.

180. BELL. *Bronze.* Ht. 3½". *CNHM* 89727.

*

Pyramidal-shaped bell with a low-relief "knob" on the front panel. No clapper.

181. BELL. *Bronze.* Ht. 3¾". *CNHM* 89728.

*

Pyramidal-shaped bell with a face in low relief at the center of the front panel. The clapper is a screw.

182. BELL. *Bronze.* Ht. 3⅝″. *CNHM* 89730.
Similar to 174. Clapper of two slender pieces of iron.

183. BELL. *Bronze.* Ht. 4⅜″. *CNHM* 89731.
Similar to 174 but with a spiral in the loop. No clapper.

184. BELL. *Bronze.* Ht. 4½″. *CNHM* 89732.
*
Pyramidal-shaped bell with flaring sides. An African face in low relief decorates the front panel, at the center.

185. BELL. *Bronze.* Ht. 4⅜″. *CNHM* 89735.
Similar to 174, but with the loop compressed. Iron clapper.

186. BELL. *Bronze.* Ht. 4⅜″. *CNHM* 89738.
Similar to 185.

187. BELL. *Bronze.* Ht. 4⅜″. *CNHM* 89736.
Pyramidal-shaped bell with flaring sides, decorated with low-relief rosette-like forms. On the front panel, at the center, in low-relief line, is a rudimentary face. Slender iron clapper.

188. BELL. *Bronze.* Ht. 5″. *CNHM* 89739.
Similar to 184. Slender iron clapper.

189. BELL. *Bronze.* Ht. 5⅜″. *CNHM* 89740.
Pyramidal-shaped bell with panels elaborately chased with guilloche variations and foliate forms. On the front panel, in low relief, is an African head surrounded by a rope form. No clapper.

190. BELL. *Bronze.* Ht. 5⅜″. *CNHM* 89742.
Plate XXXVI
Similar to 188, but the head on the front panel is larger and bearded. Above and below it, in relief, are two looped spirals, the upper one having a spiral form just below the loop. Iron clapper.

191. BELL. *Bronze.* Ht. 5¾″. *CNHM* 89741.
Plate XXXVI
Similar to 190 with two looped spiral motifs similar to the upper one in 190. No clapper.

192. BELL. *Bronze.* Ht. 5¾″. *CNHM* 89743.
Similar to 189. Slender iron clapper.

193. BELL. *Bronze.* Ht. 6⅛″. *CNHM* 89744.
Pyramidal-shaped bell with flaring sides, decorated in a similar fashion to 178 but on a lattice-work panel. No clapper.

194. BELL. *Bronze.* Ht. 7⅛″. *CNHM* 89745.
Pyramidal-shaped bell with panels of pierced lattice. On the front panel, in low relief, is an African face surrounded by a rope form. Cf. 189. Iron clapper.

195. BELL. *Bronze.* Ht. 7⅝″. *CNHM* 89746.
Pyramidal-shaped bell with marked flaring of the sides. Similar to 194, but decorated with large bosses on the sides of each panel and the handle. No clapper.

196. BELL. *Bronze.* Ht. 8¾″. *CNHM* 89747.
Rather similar to 195, but the panels are not pierced and the bosses are absent. No clapper.

197. BELL. *Bronze.* Ht. 2″. *CNHM* 89751.
Small round conical bell, of the type worn suspended from tassels, e.g., 253 and 254. No clapper.

198. BELL. *Brass.* Ht. 3⅜″. *CNHM* 89754.
*
Round bell, conical in shape and undecorated. The clapper is a nail. There would appear to be quite an amount of lead in the brass.

199. BELL. *Bronze.* Ht. 6¾″. *CNHM* 91248.
Similar to 187.

Drum

200. DRUM. *Wood, Skin, Sennit.* Ht. 5¼".
Diam. of head 4". *Fuller* R.1/68.
A small drum carved of wood with a skin tympanum retained by sennit which passes round the body of the drum over wooden pegs. The pegs are used to increase or lessen the tension on the head and hence heighten or lower the tone. "*Benin.* Small and very old Drum. The description with it was: 'Drum, African, from Benin.' Cut out of the solid piece of wood and covered with a human scalp. The beaters are made from the shell of a nut attached to a piece of string. The so-called 'beaters' merely form a rattle and the statement as to the 'scalp' is doubtful. From the Taphonse Collection of Musical Instruments, Oxford, and depicted in W. D. Webster's Catalogue No. 21, fig. 155" (Fuller).

Gongs

201. GONG. *Iron.* L. 19½". *CNHM* 89755.
No clapper.

202. GONG. *Bronze.* L. 10¼". *Fuller.*
R.2/69.
One side is chased with variations of a diamond form, the other with an angular guilloche running down the center and stippled spots, resembling a leopard's spots. No clapper.

Idiophones

203. IDIOPHONE. *Bronze.* Ht. 5⅝". *Fuller.*
R.2/31.
This piece is only the head and neck of an ibis, holding a pellet in its mouth. It is assumed that this is part of an idiophone, as, for example, 205, but, if so, it would probably have been one of rather large size. Possibly this is solely part of a casting in the round of an ibis. "*Benin.* Bird's head of large size (see Oldman's Cat. 27, August 1905. No. 16. 1905)" (Fuller).

204. IDIOPHONE. *Bronze.* Ht. 13¼". *Fuller.* R.2/66.
Plate V

An idiophone formed of a handle surmounted by an ibis with a pellet in its mouth and its wings spread.

205. IDIOPHONE. *Bronze.* Ht. 13¾". *Fuller.* R.2/65.
Plate V
Similar to 207, but with a spiral handle instead of a plain one. There is a piece of square brass, like a nut, with a screw thread inside it, at the base; this is probably not indigenous workmanship. A thin piece of metal joins the tips of the wings; this may be a runner left by the brass-smith.

206. IDIOPHONE. *Bronze.* Ht. 13⅞". *Fuller.* R.2/64.
As 207 and with a brass-screw thread as R.2/64.

207. IDIOPHONE. *Bronze.* Ht. 12¼". *Fuller.* R.2/63.
Similar to 205.

208. IDIOPHONE. *Bronze.* Ht. 13¼". *CNHM* 89799.
Similar to 207, save that the edges of the wings are much straighter and the tips of the feathers may have been broken off.

209. IDIOPHONE. *Bronze.* Ht. 13⅝". *CNHM* 89800.
Similar to 207.

Rattles

210. RATTLE. *Ivory.* L. 9¼". W. 1⅛". *CNHM* 91272.
At the top is a knob; below, the handle is carved in the form of a spiral. Inside the short base is an ivory clapper shaped like a ball. The ivory is dark brown in color.

211. RATTLE. *Bronze.* L. 7". Max. W. 3¼". *Fuller.* R.2/26.
The top part of a bronze *uxurhe* consisting of a hand holding a mud fish.

212. RATTLE. *Bronze, Iron,* L. 24¾". *CNHM* 89801.
An *uxurhe* of bronze cast on an iron rod as an armature. At the top is a right hand with the fingers bent over into the palm

and the thumb sticking up. One of the three sides of the chamber, where the rattle's pellet would have been, is missing. On one side is chased a guilloche design, the other is crosshatched.

213. RATTLE. *Bronze, Iron.* L. 19". *CNHM* 89802.

*

Stem of an *uxurhe* of bronze cast on an iron rod but with the chamber and top missing.

214. RATTLE. *Wood.* L. 52⅜". *Fuller.* R.1/30.

Plate XI

An *uxurhe* carved of wood with a double chamber surmounted by a clenched right hand similar to 212.

215. RATTLE. *Wood.* L. 49⅜". *Fuller.* R.1/31.

Plate XI

A very finely carved *uxurhe* with a double chamber surmounted by a right hand clutching a mud fish as 283. The Oba's mark, as on the ivory tusk 311, is on the side near the bottom in low relief, with, just above it, a quatrefoiled looped inter lace, also in relief.

216. RATTLE. *Wood.* L. 56½". *Fuller.* R.1/29.

Plate XI

An *uxurhe* with a single chamber carved with three figures at approximately equi-distances apart. The top figure, which is at the top of the chamber, above the chamber, is a king seated on a throne which closely resembles that on which the ivory king (105, Plate XII) is seated. In his left hand he holds an *uxurhe* which has a human head at the top. The second figure down—halfway down the shaft—is naked; his genitals are clearly shown. In his left hand he holds up an *ada* and in his right hand a stick. Below is the third figure, who is shown playing a drum. "Wooden staff with rattle. Figure of Juju Priest at the top holding Staff. Executioner middle (sword in left hand). Bottom, figure of tom-tom player. 28.1.32" (Fuller).

217. RATTLE, *Wood.* L. 47⅝". *Fuller.* R.1/32.

Plate XI

An *uxurhe* with a double chamber surmounted by a human head.

218. RATTLE. *Wood.* L. 49¾". *Fuller.* R.1/33.

Similar to 217 but with a single chamber.

219. RATTLE. *Wood.* L. 43⅞". *CNHM* 89719.

Similar to 218.

220. RATTLE. *Wood.* L. 38". *CNHM* 89720.

Similar to 218.

221. RATTLE. *Wood, Cowries, Cotton,* L. 46". *CNHM* 89721.

Plate XI

A wooden rattle, assumed to be carved in a fashion similar to 218, surmounted by a human head and covered from below the head to the bottom of the shaft with cowrie shells sewn to a cord of cotton which coils round the rattle.

Whistles

222. WHISTLE. *Bronze.* L. 9½". *Fuller.* R.3/16.

A side-blast whistle of cast bronze. "Benin bronze horn. Possibly originally in the hands of a bronze figure. 6 Oct. 1931" (Fuller).

223. WHISTLE. *Ivory.* L. 13⅛". *Fuller.* R.3/17.

A side-blast whistle. "*W. Africa* Benin? ivory whistle or horn. 9 May, 1924" (Fuller).

224. WHISTLE. *Ivory.* L. 11⅛". *Fuller.* R.3/18.

A side-blast whistle decorated in low relief with a snake on either side of the hole.

225. WHISTLE. *Ivory.* L. 13½". *Fuller.* R.3/19.

A side-blast whistle with four bands of cowrie shells in low relief at the large end (refer to 105, Plate XII), and, above, a snake or knot motif.

226. WHISTLE, *Ivory* (?). L. 9⅝″. *CNHM* 89716.
Similar to 224.

227. WHISTLE. *Ivory* (?). L. 7⅞″. *CNHM* 91273.
Similar to 226 but with only one snake.

ORNAMENTAL MASKS

Ornamental masks are either carved from ivory or cast of bronze. There are no examples of ivory masks in the two collections; they are rare in the corpus of **Benin** art and were only worn by the Oba. The famous Seligman mask was referred to in the text, and the other member of the pair is in the British Museum. It is generally thought that they were worn as pectorals, though perhaps one was suspended on the chest and the other on the back. There is, however, no direct evidence for this in the dictionary of the earlier art, namely, the plaques. The plaques do, however, show ornamental masks worn at the left hip; for example, the plaque 252 shows a bearded warrior with such a mask worn at the left hip with, below it, a bell. Ornamental masks were and are worn in this fashion by chiefs on ceremonial occasions. They were cast of bronze or brass.

Bronze ornamental masks generally have a border of eyelets to which were attached crotals, as depicted in the aforementioned plaque, 252. Such crotals are nearly always absent from the masks that survive to us. Generally, the pupils of the eyes are iron nailheads, and, in certain cases, a copper strip, which is chased by crosshatched lines, runs down the nose. These nails and strips are set in the wax before casting.

Ornamental masks have two fairly large eyelets at the back, one at the top and one at the bottom, for attachment at the left hip of the wearer.

All the ornamental masks represented in the two collections, except 235, 236, and 237, have, in varying degrees, representations of clusters of coral beads on the headdress comparable to similar clusters appearing on memorial heads and on such as the figure of an Oba (104); they also have bands of coral beads round the forehead. The forms of the headdresses of ornamental masks are represented on the plaques.

228. ORNAMENTAL MASK. *Bronze.* L. 7″. Max. W. 4½″. *Fuller.* R.2/42.
An ornamental mask of an African face with a collar of seven mud fish which protrude beyond the collar. The edge of the collar has a border of eyelets for the attachment of crotals. Iron pupils. *"Benin City.* Bronze mask pendant of Negroid appearance and with mud fish round face. Middle Period. The three large coral beads are very small in this specimen. The nose is undecorated. From the collection of Sir Cecil H. Armitage, K.B.E., D.S.O. etc., Govr & C. in C. of Gambia, of Manor House Cottage, Redcombe, Cirencester, Glos. 8 May, 1933" (Fuller).

229. ORNAMENTAL MASK. *Bronze.* L. 9¼″. Max. W. 6⅜″. *Fuller.* R.2/43.
An ornamental mask of an African face with a collar similar to that of 228 but of nine mud fish, three of which have been broken off. This piece is interesting for the fact that four of the original mud fish have been broken off, either, perhaps, during casting or as a result of wear. In their place mud-fish forms have been cast separately and riveted into place. The heads of the copper rivets

have been chased with stipple marks to simulate the stippling of the original forms. The pupils of the eyes are of iron, the upper eyelids have been chased; above each are three supraorbital keloids, which likewise are chased. A chased strip of copper runs down the nose.

"Benin City. Bronze mask pendant of large size and fine workmanship. Note marks over the eyes and cords at the ears. Pentagon headdress and nine mud fish round collar, four of which are applied but three mostly broken off. Eyes looking down. Early period. From collection of Sir Cecil H. Armitage, . . . 8 May 1933. I sold the two poorest and latest for more than I gave for the five" (Fuller).

230. ORNAMENTAL MASK. *Bronze.* L. 7⅛". Max. W. 4⅛". *Fuller. R.2/40.* An ornamental mask of an African face, probably of relatively recent date, with a collar of ten rudimentary mud-fish forms (possibly frogs) and no eyelets. The pupils appear to be chased and not of iron.

231. ORNAMENTAL MASK. *Bronze.* L. 7½". Max. W. 4⅜". *Fuller. R.2/41.* An ornamental mask of an African face with a collar in the form of a ruff, bordered by eyelets. It has iron pupils and a chased nasal strip of copper. *"Benin City.* Bronze mask pendant, incised markings over eyes and w. a plain ruff. Middle Period. From the collection of Sir Cecil H. Armitage. 8 May, 1933" (Fuller).

232. ORNAMENTAL MASK. *Bronze.* L. 7⅛". Max. W. 4¾". *CNHM 89793.* An ornamental mask of an African face with marked prognathism. Similar collar to 231. The pupils of the eyes are chased. Two forms project down from each side of the cap onto the cheek and represent the projections found on memorial heads of post-Osemwede times (e.g., 124, Plate XXXV). This piece would appear to be of relatively recent manufacture.

233. ORNAMENTAL MASK. *Bronze.* L. 7⅛". Max. W. 4¾". *CNHM 91269.* An ornamental mask of an African face similar to 229.

234. ORNAMENTAL MASK. *Bronze.* L. 7⅞". Max. W. 5¼". *CNHM 91270.* An ornamental mask of an African face with a ruff collar similar to 231, but with, in addition, seven mud fish projecting outward from the edge. Pupils are of iron but there is no nasal strip of copper. An unusual feature is the presence of two eyelets on each side of the cap intended for the suspension of the mask (cf. Seligman mask). However, two holes have been made at the back, one at the top and one at the bottom, intended, probably, as a means of suspension in the usual manner for this type of object.

235. ORNAMENTAL MASK. *Bronze.* L. 6¾" Max. W. 4¾". *CNHM 89794.* *

A poorly cast ornamental mask of an African face, probably of relatively recent manufacture. The collar has been reduced to a wavy line in relief with an outer enclosing one. The pupil of the eye is chased.

236. ORNAMENTAL MASK. *Bronze.* L. 6¼". Max. W. 4". *CNHM 89795.* *

Similar to 235 but a bit better cast.

237. ORNAMENTAL MASK. *Bronze.* L. 5¾". Max. W. 4½". *CNHM 89796.* Similar to 235 except that the collar continues right round the head and a beard is indicated. A fault below the beard suggests a repair having been made by burning in.

238. ORNAMENTAL MASK. *Bronze.* L. 5⅜". Max. W. 3⅝". *CNHM 89797.* *
Similar to 231.

239. ORNAMENTAL MASK. *Bronze.* L. 7¾". Max. W. 5¼". *Fuller. B.0/39.* **Plate XXII**

This piece is rather similar to 234, but the ruff collar is bordered by eight mud fish, each with two heads. It is, however, a much finer piece than 234. The pupils of the eyes are of iron and a finely chased strip of copper runs down the nose. The eyelids are chased, and above each are three keloids. The border of the head-dress is finely chased. *"Great Benin. A mask pendant of the finest type and workmanship. The eyes are inlaid iron and double catfish ornamentation round the neck is interesting. (See H. L. Roth's 'Great Benin,' p. 34, fig. 47; Pitt-Rivers, 'Works of Art of Benin,' fig. 87.) 29 Nov. 1920"* (Fuller). Later: *"A very fine early specimen having the usual iron inlay in the eyes and also has a bar of copper inlaid along the nose"* (Fuller). From the Bankfield Museum, collected by Dr. Roth.

240. ORNAMENTAL MASK. *Brass.* L. 7¾". Max. W. 5¾". *Fuller.* R.3/33.
Similar to 239 though not such an expressive piece of the brass-caster's art.

241. ORNAMENTAL MASK. *Brass.* L. 7". Max. W. 5". *Fuller.* R.2/37.
An ornamental mask of a leopard's face with a ruff collar, similar to 231, with a border of eyelets. Around the head, from the level of the eyes, is a border of thirteen spirals in low relief but in relief around the edges. The pupils are of iron. The mask is worn on the left hip (cf. 252 and soldier's shirt and cf. 254, Plate XXXIII). Two suspension eyelets are placed on each side of the eyes between the ruff border and the border round the top of the head (cf. 234).

PENDANTS

At certain ceremonies the Oba wears a number of objects suspended from a band round the waist. One type of object worn is the pendant plaque (see under "Plaques"), which was of ivory or bronze. The three figures in plaque 250 (Plate I) are shown wearing such pendant plaques. Another type of object worn suspended at the waist is a small conical pendant of ivory. Pendants of this type, cast of brass, were also made; notable examples are in the Egerton collection.

A number of these pendants were worn at one time. Those in the CNHM collection were carved of ivory (except 246) and carved to receive inlaid pieces of copper.

242. PENDANT. *Ivory.* L. 3⅜". *Fuller.* R.3/27.
Originating from the collection of Commander Richardson.

243. PENDANT. *Ivory.* L. 3½". *Fuller.* R.3/28.
Carved to receive pieces of cast brass. Originating from the collection of Commander Richardson.

244. PENDANT. *Ivory.* L. 3½". *Fuller.* R.3/29.
Similar to 242.

245. PENDANT. *Ivory.* L. 3⅜". *Fuller.* R.3/30.
Similar to 242.

246. PENDANT. *Bone*(?) L. 3⅝". *CNHM* 91274.
*
Similar to 242 but from a different carver's hand.

PLAQUES

This section of the itemized listing of specimens includes examples of the plaques proper, fragments of the plaques proper, pendant plaques, shield plaques, and plaques of beaten brass.

Plaques. By "plaques proper" is meant that body of objects made in the sixteenth and seventeenth centuries which were used to decorate, as Dapper (Roth, 1903: 160) has described, "beautiful and long square galleries, about as large as the Exchange at Amsterdam, but one larger than another, resting on wooden pillars, from top to bottom covered with cast copper, on which are engraved the pictures of their war exploits and battles, and are kept very clean." All the plaques which survive to us either are encrusted with the red earth of Benin or are dulled with the patina of climate and time. The bright color of bronze when freshly cast can produce startling effects of reflection and color. If the gallery in which they were observed by Dapper held any of the restful glooming from the strong sun which most buildings in Benin City have today, then the clean plaques must have given aesthetic qualities to these remarkable objects at which we can only guess.

A general estimate, made at one time by Fagg, of the number of plaques produced is put at one thousand. Two types can be distinguished: in the one the plaque had two flanges, one on either side, which, it is assumed, went round the edges of the pillar to which it was affixed; in the other there are no flanges and the average width is less than the flanged type. In the second and smaller type only single figures or items are pictured; in the larger type one or more main forms may be shown. Both types were affixed to pillars by means of nails driven through the front of the plaque. Item 282 is part of such a nail or rivet, which was obtained from one of the holes made by nailing the plaques to the supporting pillars of the gallery.

In the two collections there are twenty-nine examples of plaques in varying degrees of completeness to-gether with seven fragments. These plaques are fairly representative of the wide range of subject matter to be found throughout the total corpus. The plaques depict the people who attended the king's court—the chiefs, the warriors, their retainers—the costumes they wore, and the weapons they carried and also some of the kings themselves (e.g., 250). A number of plaques (e.g., 247, 249) depict Europeans, and it is assumed that these are Portuguese, the first western Europeans to visit Benin City. Three examples of representations of Europeans are included in the Fuller Collection (247, 281, and 249), and it seems probable that these were fairly early examples of the casting of plaques by the Edo. They are noticeable for their relatively low relief, in comparison with others which are much fuller in relief and maybe later in time. Read and Dalton (1899: 18) have identified the costume worn by some of the Europeans on the plaques as sixteenth century in style.

Apart from human beings and their various items of costume, there are a number of plaques which depict individual items of costume, such as weapons, the scabbards in which they were carried (e.g., 275), ceremonial swords such as 320, items such as a gong (266), and a collar of leopard's teeth with a rectangular bell suspended from it, as shown worn in 253.

A number of plaques of animals were cast. In the two collections there are two plaques of snakes (Plates VII and XLIV), one of the head of a crocodile (Plate VII) and three of fish, two representing parrot-fish forms

(Plate XXXIV), and the other two intertwined mud fish (Plate XIII).

A particularly striking feature of the plaques is the variety of costumes portrayed and the almost infinite variety of headdresses. Hats were apparently imported in some numbers by the Edo.

A feature sometimes overlooked, because of its commonness, is the floral background with which nearly all the plaques are decorated. There are, however, a few plaques which are decorated with the motif of a circle with a cross in it. In the two collections there is only one example of this decorative form, namely, plaque 267 (Plate VII).

A keen observer will perceive that a number of decorative motifs which appear on the costumes of figures of plaques occur on a variety of other objects of the art. A frequent motif on the borders of kilts of figures on plaques is the guilloche, sometimes chased, sometimes in low relief. This motif has a number of variations but is probably the most used decorative design in all Benin art.

Fragments of Plaques. Frequent items in collections of Benin art are parts of plaques which have been broken off from the main form.

Among the fragments included here, that of the rivet has been mentioned above, and the part of a flange which has been filed and shows the bright quality of the metal used, was mentioned in the text. Two fragments are representative of motifs used to decorate, in low relief, corners of plaques. One, 277, is in the form of a rosette and is of common occurrence. The other, 281, which is infrequently used, depicts the head and torso of a European. A fine piece of modeling and casting is 279 (Plate XLVIII), which represents a retainer heralding the progress of his chief by blowing a side-blast horn.

Pendant Plaques. Pendant plaques are worn suspended from the waist, as mentioned under "Pendants." All are shaped in the form of a shield and rise, at the top center, to form a largish suspension eyelet. Sometimes this is cunningly concealed behind the head of the central form, e.g., 288, 284, 286, 287. All have a border of eyelets to which crotals were attached.

Five types can be distinguished among the pendant plaques in the two collections. In the first type, animal forms only are depicted: 292, 290, and 291. In the second type, of which the three examples, 284, 285, and 286 (Plate XXX), are incomplete, having been broken, three kings are meant to be shown, the two outer ones supporting the arms of the central figure in a fashion similar to the depiction in plaque 250 which they closely resemble. In the third type, a female figure, probably that of a queen-mother, is represented, wearing strands of beads crossing on the chest and a coral-bead cap; on either side of the figure, in low relief, is a frog. In two of the three examples, 288 and 287 (Plate XXX), the figure is shown holding up a square object in the right hand (mirror?), but in the third, 289, she holds a circular kola-nut box, on her left side, with both hands.

The fourth type of pendant plaque, which is rare (283, Plate XVI), depicts a European astride a horse. The horse appears on certain ivory armlets, e.g., 3 and 4. It also was cast in the round with a warrior riding on it; notable examples are in the British Museum and the Nigerian Museum.

The fifth type of pendant plaque is represented by a style which is intermediary between the above four types of the two collections and the shield plaques referred to below. 296, which depicts the bottom half of Oba Ohĕ, is related to 294, which is of the Ife-Benin style, and recalls to mind certain "bespectacled" figures of probable Yoruba origin. A noticeable feature, consisting of a ladder-like border to the kilt, associates this object with what William Fagg has called the Huntsman style. This ladder-like decoration is a distinctive element on a very fine casting of a huntsman with a deer on his shoulders in the British Museum (see also under "Styles of the Benin Region"). Plaque 293, which shows a crocodile head surrounded by a guilloche border, is similar to the pendant plaque, 292, in that it portrays the same subject but lacks the border of eyelets, only having seven such forms. The guilloche border, though not in full relief, suggests an affinity with the Ife-Benin style of shield plaque.

Shield Plaques. There are five interesting pieces of casting in the two collections, all of which appear to be fragments of shield plaques. Though the pendant plaques have been described as being in the form of a shield, the distinction "shield plaque" as used here applies to a form larger in shape and more hemispherical than the conventional description; in addition, the term is used for objects or parts of objects which relate to a style represented by a fine plaque in the Benin Museum. The Benin shield plaque is interesting for the striations on the central figure which are similar to those appearing on the bronze heads and figures of Ife, a feature which, in part, leads to the feeling that the plaque might have originated from Ife or, though Benin work, be strongly influenced by the Ife style. The Benin plaque probably represents Oba Ohĕ, who is associated with the god Olokŭ, the god of the sea and waters. On the plaque is represented the mud fish, a royal emblem, which would appear to be the symbolic representation of the god. In the British Museum is a shield plaque of more recent date than the Benin Museum piece; in style it is definitely assignable as Edo work; in subject matter it has much in common with the Benin Museum piece (see Forman, W. and B., and Dark, 1960: 40). Plaque 295 has a number of features in common with the aforementioned shield plaques, as well as being similar in style to the Ife-Benin piece; notably the striated head, the tail ends of two mud fish with most of the body of one, an elephant head with a trunk ending in a human hand holding an object, and a guilloche border. The three last mentioned motifs appear on the flanged bases of memorial heads. Such heads are not, however, the earliest in time of the generally accepted sequence of memorial heads. The Benin shield plaque and the fragments listed below would, however, appear to be earlier in time than the flanged base memorial heads.

Beaten-Brass Plaques. Reference has been made in the text to plaques of beaten brass and their use.

Plaques

247. PLAQUE. *Bronze.* Ht. 16¾″. W. 14″. *Fuller.* R.0/63.
Plates XXVI, XXVII
This plaque depicts two Europeans, the taller of whom holds a staff in his right hand and with his left clutches the hand of the smaller of the two figures. Above the latter is a fish with a snake in its mouth. This fish is similar to that on plaque 270, where it is the sole subject matter. Fish of this type do occasionally form a corner motif of plaques, but its size on this plaque is rather singular. A unique feature is the representation of two Europeans with such disparity between their sizes. The right arm of the taller of the two figures suggests that a fault occurred in the casting resulting from a slight movement of the investment. The back of the plaque shows no such movement. The square beard of the taller figure is unusual, the shape of the beard of his companion being a more common form. The taller figure appears to have a small hunting horn attached to his belt, on the right side. Attached to the belt of the smaller figure is, on the right side, a pouch behind which is a dagger in a sheath; on his left side is a long-necked flask with a strap held in his left hand.

248. PLAQUE. *Bronze.* Ht. 15⅝″. W. 7½″. *Fuller.* R.0/65.
Plate XLVI
Though the costume worn by the figure represented on this plaque is European and his beard is of a form associated with Europeans, the facial features are strongly Negroid: the alae of the nose are broad, though the nose is long and narrow. The hat of this figure appears to be representative of civilian dress in con-

trast to the military helmets worn by the two figures in 247. The figure fingers his beard with the left hand; in his right hand is a short stick. His jacket is undone.

249. PLAQUE. *Bronze.* Ht. 15⅝″. W. 11⅜″. *Fuller.* R.0/66.
Plate XXXVIII
The costume worn by the European represented on this plaque is similar to that shown on 248; similarly, the figure carries a short stick in his right hand. The hat, however, is different and is shown with a cord leading down either side of the face and passing under the beard. Four mud fish are used to decorate the four corners of the plaque. Cf. 273.

250. PLAQUE. *Bronze.* Ht. 16¼″. W. 13½″. *CNHM 8258.*
Plate I
A plaque depicting three kings wearing tall bead caps and bead shirts. The two outer figures are supporting the arms of the central figure, who holds in his right hand a blacksmith's hammer, the head of which has been broken off. The feature of a support and runner to this hammer from the back of the plaque is similar to that referred to for 262. Hanging around the waists of the three figures are pendant plaques: of crocodiles, on the two outer figures, and of three European heads, on the central figure. A good portion of a flange of this plaque survives; it is decorated with a guilloche motif, the motif generally chased on such flanges. Cf. Forman, W. and B., and Dark, 1960: Plates 30 and 31.

251. PLAQUE. *Bronze.* Ht. 15¾″. W. 6¾″. *Fuller.* R.0/67.
This plaque shows the figure of a chief wearing a coral-bead cap from which hang strings of beads. In his right hand he holds a stick which is in relief but supported by short runners from the back of the plaque in a similar fashion referred to for 250 and 262.

252. PLAQUE. *Bronze.* Ht. 15¼″. W. 9⅛″. *Fuller.* R.0/68.

The plaque depicts a bearded soldier supporting with his left hand on top of his head what is probably the representation of a kola pod. The sword at his waist would stick out horizontally behind, as can be seen from the figure in the round (102, Plate XLV). At his left hip he wears an ornamental mask of an African face, attached to which are small crotals, and, below, a round bell. The rosette form in the right-hand top corner of the plaque is the most typical of forms used to decorate the corners of plaques. Examples of other bearded figures, who generally seem to be associated with warfare, are in the British Museum (*vide* Read and Dalton, 1899, and Forman, W. and B., and Dark, 1960: Plate 42). The investment supporting this plaque when it was cast may have sunk because, on the right-hand side of the plaque, there appear to be two layers of metal.

253. PLAQUE. *Bronze.* Ht. 16½″. W. 7¼″. *Fuller.* R.0/69.
This plaque shows a chief in the garb of a soldier; the hilt of his sword can be seen in the crook of his left arm, which holds a ceremonial sword (*ebẽ*). Below his coral-bead choker he wears a collar of leopard's teeth and a band across his chest from which is suspended a rectangular bell (see 102, Plate XLV). This is worn on top of a shirt similar in form to that of 254 but lacking the delineation of the features of the face of a leopard which are shown on that plaque. Attached to his anklets are tassels or small crotals. The strange lack of completion of the rosette in the right-hand bottom corner and left-hand top one suggests that this plaque may have been cut down for some reason in the wax before casting.
"*Great Benin.* Bronze plaque of a figure of a noble? in full court dress holding an Ebere (*ebẽ*) in his left hand. For its size the plaque is very heavy. An almost similar specimen sold Sotheby's 6/12/1954 for £450. 19 Nov., 1920" (Fuller).

254. PLAQUE. *Bronze.* Ht. 16¾″. W. 7¼″. *Fuller.* R.0/70.
Plates XXXII, XXXIII
Another example of a plaque of a chief in the garb of a warrior. In his left hand he holds, across his body, a sword similar in form to that of 102 (Plate XLV). In his right hand he holds a flail(?). Two half-moons decorate the bottom two corners of the plaque, and one may have been broken off from the top left-hand corner. As with the rosettes of the previous plaque, 253, it would seem that the left-hand side of the plaque may have been cut down in the wax, for only half the moon is shown.
"*Benin City.* Bronze plaque collected by Dr. J. G. Whittendale, late of Lime House, Bishop's Waltham. 28 April, 1917" (Fuller).

255. PLAQUE. *Bronze.* Ht. 20¾″. W. 7⅝″. *Fuller.* R.0/72.
The figure of this plaque has a rather elongated appearance. He is naked to the waist; he has a single strand of beads round his neck; on each arm he wears an armlet. Above each eye are three keloids. His hair is plaited into two strands on the left and one on the right. Formerly in the Bankfield Museum (see Roth, 1903: Fig. 156).

256. PLAQUE. *Bronze.* Ht. 7¾″. W. 5⅛″. *Fuller.* R.0/75.
Part of a plaque showing the upper half of a chief. It would appear that he was holding in his left hand a sword (*ada*). Two feathers can be seen sticking out of his cap. Cf. 253.

257. PLAQUE. *Bronze* L. 15⅝″. W. 11¼″. CNHM 89771.
Plaque of a figure very similar to 255—the right hand is in a similar position—but wearing bracelets instead of armlets and with the left arm around a sword. A strap crosses from his right shoulder to the sword on his left side.

258. PLAQUE. *Bronze.* L. 16½″. W. 7¼″. CNHM 89772.
A plaque very similar to 255, but with

two plaits on each side of the head, bracelets instead of armlets, and clearly chased cicatrization marks on the body. The finely chased motifs on his kilt—a quatrefoil and an abstract head—are similar to those on 265 and 264.

259. PLAQUE. *Bronze.* L. 11¼″. W. 5½″. *CNHM* 89773.

Top portion of a plaque with a figure in a similar position to 255, wearing armlets, a high collar, a band of coral beads round the forehead and a very wide necklace, reaching almost to the navel, composed of two lengths of large oval beads bordered by smaller ones. A feather on the left side of the figure's cap has been broken off.

260. PLAQUE. *Bronze.* Ht. 15⅜″. W. 7½″. *CNHM* 91242.

Plate XLI

Plaque of a figure of a chief, wearing a tall cap decorated with cowrie shells(?), holding up an *ebẽ* in his right hand and grasping with his left hand held out to the side a spear, the top part of which has been broken off. His costume is somewhat similar to that on 254. The design on the bell worn on his chest is similar to that on the front panel of bell 186. The head of a crocodile fills the bottom right-hand corner of the plaque. Illustrated in Webster's *Catalogue,* V, 38, Fig. 28.

261. PLAQUE. *Bronze.* Ht. 13¾″. W. 6¼″. *CNHM* 91244.

Part of a plaque showing all but the feet of a figure who is bearded and holds in front of him, in both hands, an object which is indecipherable though suggestive of a dish. He wears a feather on the left side of the head and on each arm a bracelet. Illustrated in Webster's *Catalogue,* IV, 84, Fig. 5.

262. PLAQUE. *Bronze.* Ht. 13¼″. W. 5″. *CNHM* 91245.

Part of a plaque which shows the complete figure of a man, save the right foot, holding in his right hand a staff, which is in relief and well out from the back of

the plaque and held in position by two supports (*vide* 251). He wears a high collar and "bowler" (derby) hat. Illustrated in Webster's *Catalogue,* IV, 84, Fig. 80.

263. PLAQUE. *Bronze.* Ht. 16⅞″. W. 13⅜″. *CNHM* 91247.

Plaque of a figure resembling that on 255, except that the hair is not plaited and the right hand is turned outward, so that the palm is visible, and, with it, he holds up a long stick. The left-hand top corner and the bottom two corners are decorated with rosettes in relief, the whole plaque being much wider than 255. Illustrated in Webster's *Catalogue,* Vol. III, No. 18, Fig. 69.

264. PLAQUE. *Bronze.* Ht. 13¾″. W. 9″. *CNHM* 91263.

Part of a plaque showing most of one figure, save the lower legs and feet, and half of another one. Both wear high collars, long necklaces of coral beads, and armlets; their arms and bodies are covered with a diamond pattern filled with circles. Both wear on their hair a "spike" which was made of fiber. The right-hand figure holds a rattle(?) in his left hand. On each side of the head of the left-hand figure is a coil of hair. At the waist of the right-hand figure are five bells: three are rectangular in shape, the other two are round and small.

265. PLAQUE. *Bronze.* Ht. 14⅛″. W. 6¼″. *CNHM* 91268.

Plate III

Part of a plaque showing the figure of a chief, save his lower legs and feet, holding in his hands a small calabash rattle: "The rattle mentioned by D. R. . . . ." This was an ordinary round calabash with a loose net over it, and at each knot was a small seed or cowrie. The instrument was held and shaken in both hands and made a crisp sound . . . "C.P." (Roth, 1903: caption to Fig. 103). He wears a necklace of smaller clapper bells, similar to those at the waist of the right-hand figure of 264, and has a conical point to his bead cap (cf. 264). The wide band going from his left shoulder across his chest was of coral beads. Cf. Forman, W. and B., and Dark, 1960: Plate 9.

266. PLAQUE. *Bronze.* Ht. 20¼″. W. 12¾″. *Fuller.* B.1/2.

Plate XV

This plaque depicts a man playing a gong very similar to the example in the round, 202; the remains of the stick with which he is striking it can be seen on the body of the gong. His shirt and other items of costume are similar to those on 254. He wears a sword which is in its sheath. Of particular interest are the corner motifs. The top right-hand part of the plaque is missing, but in each of the bottom two corners is a quatrefoil in relief, the only example(?) of the use of this motif in this way.

"*Great Benin.* Bronze plaque of a native in full dress beating a sistrum. This specimen is unusual in the large size of the figure (18″) and in having 2 *raised* quatrefoil ornaments at the lower ornaments. Formerly in the Bankfield Museum, Halifax, and obtained through the Hon. Curator, Mr. H. Ling Roth. See his book 'Great Benin' 1903, pp. 111 and 117, fig. 120 where this plaque is illustrated. 24 July 1920" (Fuller).

267. PLAQUE. *Bronze.* Ht. 11½″. W. 5″. *Fuller.* R.0/74.

Plate VII

Part of a plaque depicting a snake, a viper(?). This is the only example in the two collections of a plaque with the background motif of a circle with a cross in it. "*Benin.* An imperfect plaque with a snake. Of early date and with the rare ground work tooling. This is the only example I know of with this tooling on a plaque other than of a human being. See Oldman's Cat. 29; August 1905, No. 10. C. early 16th cent. August, 1905" (Fuller).

268. PLAQUE. *Bronze.* Ht. 16″. W. 6⅛″. *Fuller.* R.0/76.

Plate XLIV

This plaque shows a snake, similar to that on 267, with a fish in its mouth. The fish is similar to that on plaque 247.

269. PLAQUE. *Bronze.* Ht. 20⅛″. W. 11⅞″. *CNHM* 91246.

Plaque with two snakes similar to that on 267. The flange which went around the pillars to which the plaques were at one time attached, and described by Dapper, is present on this plaque. Illustrated in Webster's *Catalogue*, V, 48, Fig. 90.

270. PLAQUE. *Bronze.* Ht. 18⅛″. W. 5⅞″. *CNHM* 91243.

Plaque of a fish similar to that held in the mouth of the snake on plaque 268 and to those on plaque 271. Illustrated in Webster's *Catalogue*, IV, 87, Fig. 1.

271. PLAQUE. *Bronze.* Ht. 14½″. W. 7″. *CNHM* 89770.

Plate XXXIV

Plaque of a fish, similar to that on 270, with a very small fish of the same species in its mouth.

272. PLAQUE. *Bronze.* Ht. 12⅛″. W. 6¼″. *CNHM* 91264.

Plate XIII

Plaque depicting two interlaced mud fish; similar to 273.

273. PLAQUE. *Bronze.* Ht. 15½″. W. 6½″. *CNHM* 8259.

Similar to 272.

274. PLAQUE. *Bronze.* Ht. 18¾″. W. 7⅝″. *Fuller.* R.0/71.

Plate VII

Plaque of the head of a crocodile. A similar crocodile head appears as a corner motif on plaque 260. There are plaques in the corpus of Benin art which depict whole crocodiles. One in the British Museum, 98. 1-15.172 (*vide* Forman, W. and B., and Dark, 1960: Plate 86), shows a crocodile with a fish in its mouth similar to the fish in the mouth of the snake on plaque 268. Formerly in the Bankfield Museum: see Roth, 1903: Fig. 155.

275. PLAQUE. *Bronze.* Ht. 19¾″. W. 11¾″. *Fuller.* R.0/73.

This plaque depicts two scabbards. "*Benin.* Plaques with these objects of the ceremonial dress are rare. Sotheby's Lot 22, 26 July, 1932" (Fuller).

276. PLAQUE FRAGMENT. *Bronze.* L. 2¾″. W. 3¾″. *CNHM* 89780.

*

Part of the kilt of a figure.

277. PLAQUE FRAGMENT. *Bronze.* L. 4⅜″. W. 2⅞″. *CNHM* 89783.
A rosette, in rather high relief. Cf. 263.

278. PLAQUE FRAGMENT. *Bronze.* Ht. 4½″. W. 2 1/16″. *CNHM* 89785.
The right lower leg and foot of a figure.

279. PLAQUE FRAGMENT. *Bronze.* Ht. 6¼″. W. 3½″. *CNHM* 91251.
Plate XLVIII
A very fine piece of casting in rather high relief depicting an attendant to a chief blowing a side-blast horn. The left hand is supported from the back of the plaque. He wears a sword on the left side with, suspended from it, a round bell. The cicatrization marks on the body are clearly shown. The remains of the left-hand flanged edge of the plaque are present. Illustrated in Webster's *Catalogue,* V, 52, Fig. 128.

280. PLAQUE FRAGMENT. *Bronze.* L. 5⅜″. W. ¾″. *Fuller.* R.9/79.
Part of the flange of a plaque; it has been filed down and shows very clearly the bright quality of the metal. It is decorated with an angular guilloche motif.

281. PLAQUE FRAGMENT. *Bronze.* L. 6¾″. W. 3″. *Fuller.* R.9/78.
This fragment of a plaque depicts the head and torso of a European; the head is in profile. He wears a feather in his helmet. In his right hand he holds a pipe. This fragment decorated the right-hand corner of a plaque in a fashion similar to the rosettes on plaque 263 or the mud fish on plaque 249.

282. RIVET. *Bronze.* Max. Diam. ¼″. *Fuller.* R.9/80.

*

"*Benin.* Rivet out of a hole in a 16th century plaque of a European" (Fuller).

283. PENDANT PLAQUE. *Bronze.* L. 6¾″. W. 5⅛″. *Fuller.* R.2/36.
Plate XVI
Pendant plaque depicting a European astride a horse. In his right hand he holds a pike; at his right hip is shown his sword; with his left hand he holds the reins of the horse. The background is chased with circles, the spaces in between being filled with stippling. Two links remain in two of the eyelets which border the plaque. "*Benin.* A rare and early piece c. 1500. A Portuguese riding a horse is a very rare subject. Note knee breeches and ground work of circles like on my 15 cent. head. 1906?" (Fuller).

284. PENDANT PLAQUE. *Bronze.* Ht. 5¾″. W. 3½″. *CNHM* 89775.
Plate XXX
Part of a pendant plaque representing three kings similar to plaque 250 (Plate I). Only the top halves of the left-hand and central figures are left.

285. PENDANT PLAQUE. *Bronze.* Ht. 5½″. W. 2½″. *CNHM* 89776.
Plate XXX
Part of a pendant plaque similar to 284 above, but only the top half of the left-hand figure remains.

286. PENDANT PLAQUE. *Bronze.* Ht. 4¾″. W. 3⅜″. *CNHM* 89777.
Plate XXX
Part of a pendant plaque similar to 284 above, but only the top halves of the right-hand and central figures remain.

287. PENDANT PLAQUE. *Bronze.* Ht. 4¾″. W. 3⅛″. *CNHM* 91258.
Plate XXX
An incomplete pendant plaque, depicting a woman, holding up a square object (mirror?) in her right hand. She is wearing a coral-bead cap with bead tassels hanging from it to her shoulders, a thick, round low collar of beads and, from each shoulder and crossing on her chest, a band of coral beads. Her skirt is of very open network. To her right and below her

right arm is a frog. The left side and bottom of the pendant are missing. The round collar worn by the figure recalls that of a certain type of early head not represented in the two collections but of which, for example, there are two specimens in the Museum of Primitive Art, New York.

288. PENDANT PLAQUE. *Bronze.* Ht. 5⅜″. W. 3¾″. *CNHM* 89774
Plate XXX

Similar to 287 above though more complete, as a second frog is shown on the left side of the figure.

289. PENDANT PLAQUE. *Bronze.* Ht. 5¼″. W. 4⅛″. *CNHM* 89784.

A complete version of a pendant plaque, rather similar to 288, except that the head has been broken off, and, instead of holding up an object in the right hand, the woman holds a round object in her left hand, her right hand supporting it in front. The object probably represents a round kola-nut box. Above the frog on the right side is a boss in low relief.

290. PENDANT PLAQUE. *Bronze.* Ht. 5¾″. W. 4½″. *Fuller.* R.2/39.

Pendant plaque depicting two intertwined mud fish, similar to 292. Cf. 273. "Benin Pendant 7 May 1912. AF. 9/" (Fuller).

291. PENDANT PLAQUE. *Bronze.* Ht. 4¾″. W. 3¼″. *CNHM* 91241.

Similar to 290. Illustrated in Webster's *Catalogue,* V, 51, Fig. 110.

292. PENDANT PLAQUE. *Bronze.* Ht. 6¼″. W. 3¾″. *Fuller.* R.2/38.

Pendant plaque depicting the head of a crocodile. Cf. 274.

293. PENDANT PLAQUE. *Bronze.* Ht. 5⅛″. W. 5½″. *CNHM* 89779.

*

Pendant plaque depicting the head of a crocodile; the right-hand corner has been broken off. This piece differs from the other pendant plaques in that it has a widish border decorated by a guilloche motif in low relief and instead of a con-

tinuous border of eyelets has only eight, evenly spaced from each other.

Shield Plaques

294. SHIELD PLAQUE. *Bronze.* Ht. 10¼″. W. 6⅞″. *Fuller.* R.0/77

Fragment of a shield plaque. At the top, on the left, is an elephant's head with a spiral trunk ending in a hand holding a small globular-like object. This motif, in varying forms, appears on quite a variety of objects, notably on the flanged bases of heads CNHM 125, 122, 131, 121, 124. This particular motif may well be the forerunner of subsequent ones. To the left of the elephant's head is the remains of a ram's head. Below, on the left, is a mud fish, the tail of which curls round and up under the chin of a head which is striated. From each nostril issues a snake, but only the right-hand one remains; it curls up beside the right-hand side of the head. There are several representations in Benin art of snakes issuing from nostrils, notably a fine ornamental mask and a splendid bronze head in the British Museum (illustrated in Forman, W. and B., and Dark, 1960; Plates 81-82, 79-80). In such contexts the snake signifies magical power and is probably associated with Osū, god of medicine. There remains part of a larger border to the plaque formed of a guilloche design, pierced. This fragment is very similar to the fine shield plaque which used to be in the Liverpool Museum and was destroyed in the second World War. It is illustrated in Roth, 1903: Fig. 268. The Liverpool piece appears to be in the Huntsman style. "Benin. Half of an aegis of large size and rare type. It came from Benin, but face suggests Ife" (Fuller).

295. SHIELD PLAQUE. *Bronze.* L. 4½″. W. 3⅝″. *Fuller.* R.0/78.

Small part of a shield plaque showing an edge of eyelets, a plain border, on which, in relief, is a grasshopper and, next to it, the remains of a low-relief guilloche pattern, pierced. Fuller connected this piece with the previous one, 294: "Benin. Portion of same object, with a locust. See Oldman's Cat. 29; August 1905, No. 12, 1905" (Fuller).

296. SHIELD PLAQUE. *Bronze.* Ht. 4⅝″. W. 5⅝″. *CNHM* 89781.
Part of a small shield plaque, which really is closer in form to a pendant plaque than the shield plaques with which it is here included. It depicts, as mentioned above, the bottom half of Oba Ohĕ with mud-fish feet and, on the kilt, the "ladder" type of marking of the Huntsman style.

297. SHIELD PLAQUE. *Bronze.* Ht. 5⅛″. W. 3½″. *CNHM* 89782.
Fragment of a shield plaque with, in low relief, a round, striated face (cf. 294) and three large raised forms very similar to the scales of a crocodile though also suggestive of kola nuts.

298. SHIELD PLAQUE. *Bronze.* L. 6⅜″. W. 5¼″. *CNHM* 89798.
Fragment of a shield plaque with, in relief, a mud fish and part of a crocodile.

Beaten-Brass Plaques

299. PLAQUE. *Brass* (Beaten). L. 7½″. W. 4⅛″. *CNHM* 91253.
Plate XXI
Beaten-brass plaque in the form of a leopard's head with ears riveted to the head. The head is bordered by a series of holes through which nails may have been driven to affix the object to wood, perhaps a door of the Oba's palace.

300. PLAQUE. *Brass* (Beaten). L. 7½″. W. 4¼″. *CNHM* 91254.
Plate XXI
As 299.

301. PLAQUE. *Brass* (Beaten). Diam. 6⅝″. *CNHM* 91255.
A circular plaque of beaten brass depicting a bizarre figure holding a staff in his right hand and an unidentifiable object in his left. The decorative elements include two rosettes, and the surface is heavily stippled. Illustrated in Webster's *Catalogue,* IV, 8, Fig. 31.

302. PLAQUE. *Brass* (Beaten). Diam. 6⅝″. *CNHM* 91256.
A circular plaque of beaten brass showing the figure of a chief holding up in his right hand an *ebĕ*. The rest of the surface is decorated with six rosettes and is heavily stippled. Illustrated in Webster's *Catalogue,* IV, 8, Fig. 30.

STOOLS

The type of stool represented by the three of the Fuller Collection would appear to be relatively recent; perhaps they were made in the last quarter of the last century. The top, legs, sides, and end pieces are carved in low relief and joined; the seat is fixed firmly to the legs by large-headed iron nails, which are driven home without consideration for their place in the design on the top of the seat. A variety of figures is depicted, including rather bizarre portrayals of Europeans.

303. STOOL. *Wood.* Top: L. 25″, W. 14⅛″, Thick. 1⅛″. Ht. 13⅞″. *Fuller.* R.1/23.
Plate XIV
On the top of this seat, carved in low relief, in the center, is the figure of a European with a long pipe in his mouth, standing on a horse. In his left hand he holds a dagger and the reins of the horse, and in his right a saber. He is flanked on either side by an Edo personage: to his right, a figure with weapons—including a crossbow, shield, and spears—and, to his left, a figure with a sword in his right hand and in the left hand the top half of a figure, which has been cut in two. A musket and powder flask can be seen at the right-hand end of the top of the seat.

The legs, sides, and ends are carved in low relief with figures of Europeans and

Edo, variously armed. Of particular interest is the central medallion portion of one of the sides which depicts a naked woman with cicatrization marks on her body; on her head she carries a tray, supported by her left hand, containing kola nuts(?); to her right is a tray with a fish in it; to her left, on a stand, is an *uxurhe*, with a head at the top, another *uxurhe*, with a clenched hand at the top, and a memorial head with a tusk on it.

304. STOOL. *Wood.* Top: L. 26″, W. 12½″, Thick. 1⅛″. Ht. 14¼″. *Fuller.* R.1/24.

On the top of this seat, carved in low relief, at the center, are represented two figures, each standing on a leopard; the figure to the right is an Oba, holding in his right hand an *uxurhe* the top of which is a clenched hand; he is supported by a chief who stands to his left. To the right of the king are three figures; the center one holds a sword in his right hand and a crossbow in his left; to his right is the figure of a horseman, to his left that of a naked woman. To the king's left is a chief holding an *ebē* in his right hand; with his left hand he touches the arm of another personage.

A variety of figures is carved in low relief on the legs, sides, and ends of the seat. On one side and at one end are figures of Europeans; on the other side and at the other end are figures of Edo people, including a naked man and woman standing with an arm round each other. On the side piece joining the two legs depicting Edo people is the figure of Ofoe, the messenger of the god of death. He is shown as a head, with two feet above his head and two arms below. From each nostril issues the tail of a crocodile, which is shown on either side of his head.

305. STOOL. *Wood.* Top: L. 24⅞″, W. 13¼″, Thick. 1¼″. Ht. 15⅞″. *Fuller.* R.1/25.

This seat is carved in low relief with geometric and curvilinear designs. On the top are three bands containing guilloche motifs. The legs, sides, and ends are carved with rosette and guilloche forms and linear patterns. The sides joining the legs are of a form different from those on 303 and 304, consisting of a straight piece between each leg with a support descending from the seat to the center of the side piece. The end pieces are more angular than those of the two aforementioned seats.

TUSKS

Two principal forms of ivory tusks are represented in the two collections. The first consists of the three large tusks, 306, 307, and 308, which are carved all over in low relief with figures of past kings, both actual and mythological, of personages, and of various animal forms. Round the base of each is a low-relief guilloche. This design is the sole decoration of some tusks on which it appears in the form of three or more bands separated by intervals of plain tusk. The carved tusks were placed on the brass heads which formed part of the furniture of the king's ancestor shrines. A tusk on such a head is carved in low relief on one of the sides of the stool, 303 (Plate XIV).

The second form of tusk is plain but carved with one or two marks which are the king's mark (Roth, 1903: Fig. 96), all ivory belonging to the king.

306. TUSK. *Ivory.* L. 7′4″. *CNHM 8143.*
Plate XVII

A very fine ivory tusk carved all over with figures and animal forms. The second and fifth figures up, on the front of the tusk (on the outer side of the circumference), are representations of Oba Ohē, who was mentioned under "Shield Plaques." Figures of Europeans and other dignitaries can be seen. Other forms include crocodile heads, a clenched hand, a turkey cock, crocodile, leopard, mud fish, cock, and elephant head with the trunk ending in a human hand. In the detail of the tusk illustrated is shown the figure of a European holding the foot of a leopard with his right hand. Above his hat is the head of a crocodile. To his left is the head of an elephant with its trunk ending in a human hand. Below the figure's feet is a leaf form similar to that found on altars to the hand.

307. Tusk. *Ivory.* L. 5′6″. *CNHM* 8144.
Plate XL
Generally similar to 306 in being carved all over with figures and animal forms. The ivory of this tusk is relatively "fresh" and the carving somewhat cruder than that of 306; the general impression is that it may be relatively recent. In the detail of the tusk illustrated is the figure of an Edo holding a spear in each hand. Below him is the guilloche border to the base of the tusk.

308. Tusk. *Ivory.* L. 4′. *CNHM* 8145.
Plate XXIX
Similar to 307 but better carved. In the detail of the tusk illustrated is the figure of a soldier, holding in his right hand a spear and with his left a shield. He is depicted garbed with a soldier's shirt decorated with the markings of a leopard's head, and his cap is decorated with cowrie shells. Below his right foot are the head and upper part of the body of a European. Below his shield is a leopard. Above his cap is a guilloche motif with the feet of another figure. To the left of this figure is part of a mud fish.

309. Tusk. *Ivory.* L. 18″. *Fuller.* R.1/61.
Plain tusk, except for one Oba's mark. "Lot 333 14558 4 March 1930. *Benin with King's Mark* from Ralph Locke's collection one of the two survivors of the Massacre 4/1/1897" (Fuller).

310. Tusk. *Ivory.* L. 36⅝″. *Fuller.* R.1/62.
A dark-brown-colored tusk carved with one Oba's mark.

311. Tusk. *Ivory.* L. 28⅜″. *Fuller.* R.1/59.
A medium-brown-colored tusk carved with two Oba's marks.

312. Tusk. *Ivory.* L. 12¾″. *Fuller.* R.3/20.
*
Plain ivory tusk.

313. Tusk. *Ivory.* L. 20⅝″. *CNHM* 89717.
*
Plain tusk carved with one Oba's mark.

314. Tusk. *Ivory.* L. 15¾″. *CNHM* 89718.
*
Plain tusk carved with one Oba's mark.

WEAPONS

The weapons represented in this section can be divided into three groups. The first consists of ceremonial swords, the second contains offensive weapons, and the third, defensive arms.

Ceremonial swords are of two types: the *ebẽ*, a leaf-shaped sword (e.g., 318), and the *ada*, which has a long S-curving blade (e.g., 325) (both of which are shown in Plate XVIII). Both swords are carried by chiefs on ceremonial occasions. The *ebẽ* is the most common form, whereas the use of the *ada* is restricted to certain high-ranking chiefs. The Oba uses both. Plaque 260 shows a chief carrying an *ebẽ* in his right hand.

Both types of sword were either made from iron or cast from brass. The handles and butts were elaborated in varying degrees with beaten-brass plates or copper wire, or, on rare examples, with ivory. According to Chief Ine, chief of the brassworkers in Benin, the problem of casting an object 3 feet long was solved by modeling the form so that it bent round to half its final length in the mold and then straightening it after it was cast.

The offensive weapons are represented by seven swords—all relatively short—a dagger, three spears, two spearheads, two shrapnel charges, and a powder flask. All are made of iron, except the powder flask, which is of cast brass.

There are five examples of shields —four from the Fuller Collection and one from CNHM. The shields are made of plaited sheets of a light wood strong enough to stop an arrow. The type of shield represented here was common to a relatively wide area (e.g., Talbot, 1926: Fig. 139), as Captain Fuller noted for 346.

Ceremonial Swords

315. EBE. *Iron.* L. 39″. Max. W. 9″. *Fuller.* R.1/47.
The blade is decorated with punched marks. Bone handle. "*Benin.* An EBERE, a purely ceremonial object and much in evidence in Benin City. C. Punch records, 'they were ornaments held in the hand and turned about during ceremonial dances.' See L. Roth, Great Benin, p. 60, fig. 70 and p. 61, fig. 70a; Pitt-Rivers, p. 84, Pl. 42, figs. 326 and 7 and p. 86, pl. 43, figs. 328–9. This specimen is rather remarkable for the extensive repairs and yet the pointed end is imperfect. The handle still retains its bone covering which is often missing. Acquired in 1902" (Fuller).

316. EBE. *Iron.* L. 24¾″. Max. W. 6″. *CNHM* 89831.
The blade is decorated with punched marks with a design similar to that of 315.

317. EBE. *Iron.* L. 29⅜″. Max. W. 6⅛″. *CNHM* 89832.
Similar to 316.

318. EBE. *Iron.* L. 38″. Max. W. 8¾″. *CNHM* 89833.
Plate XVIII
Similar to 315. The blade has been repaired by riveting two large strips to it.

319. EBE. *Iron.* L. 39⅝″. Max. W. 9¼″. *CNHM* 89834.
Similar to 315. The blade has been repaired by riveting.

320. EBE. *Iron.* L. 30⅜″. Max. W. 6⅜″. *Fuller.* R.1/48.
Similar to 319. "*Benin.* An EBERE of small size—a purely ceremonial wand 'or ornament held in the hand and turned about during ceremonial dances.' (C. Punch) . . ." (see references under 315, above) (Fuller).

321. ADA. *Iron.* L. 37⅞″. *Fuller.* R.1/41.
A ceremonial sword the blade of which is of iron, the handle of wood, partially wound with brass wire, and the hilt covered with beaten brass, riveted with copper rivets. "*Benin.* Called ADA. It was an official sword carried in front of the king, and certain other high officials, by a naked youth. The sharp edge was carried outwards in the right hand, while the left hand supported the right arm under the elbow. M. C. Punch. See Roth's 'Great Benin' 190–5 (or 1903), p. 116, fig. 119. It was also used by the king's executioners. This is a fine, old and large specimen and obviously meant more for the latter use than for carrying. I think those carried were the much lighter kind of brass and much decorated. (See also Pitt-Rivers, p. 86, pl. 18, fig. 110.) 16 March, 1948" (Fuller).

322. ADA. *Iron.* L. 36⅜″. *Fuller.* R.1/42.
Like 321 but with copper wire bound round the handle. "*Benin.* An ADA of the execution type. Fine and perfect. 5 Nov. 1929" (Fuller).

323. ADA. *Iron.* L. 30½″. *Fuller.* R.1/43. Like 321 but with brass wire completely round the handle. *"Benin.* An ADA. Type used for executions with lug at end of hilt sometimes missing. 16 March 1948" (Fuller).

324. ADA. *Iron.* L. 29¼″. *Fuller.* R.1/44.
*
Iron blade of an *ada* with remains of a hilt of cast and beaten brass showing copper rivets to secure the brass. *"Benin.* Blade without the hilt of an ADA of execution type. 1902" (Fuller).

325. ADA. *Brass.* L. 34″. *Fuller.* R.1/46.
Plate XVIII
The handle of this *ada* is similar to that of 321, but the sword is cast from brass. The surface of the blade is chased with curvilinear and geometric designs, including a guilloche. The spaces around the designs are stippled. Cut out from the center of the blade is the shape of a cross. *"Benin.* A very fine ADA of brass or bronze, heavy and completely engraved, probably for ceremonial use although it might be stout enough for executions. 16 March, 1948" (Fuller).

326. ADA. *Brass.* L. 34″. *Fuller.* R.1/45. Similar to 325, except that the blade is formed of pierced lattice work and a guilloche surrounded by an edge on which guilloche motifs are chased and the spaces around are stippled. *"Benin.* A fine and rare ADA of brass obviously for ceremonial use only. 5 Nov. 1929" (Fuller).

Offensive Weapons

327. SWORD. *Iron.* L. 27⅛″. *Fuller.* R.2/70.
"Benin. An old and typical sword, carefully tooled all over the blade with 2 crocodiles and other designs. From a small collection of old Benin weapons and execution swords. 16 March 1948" (Fuller). The handle is covered with brass wire and the hilt studded with copper nails.

328. SWORD. *Iron.* L. 17⅜″. *Fuller.* R.2/74.
*
Sword with an iron blade and a brass handle.

329. SWORD. *Iron.* L. 24½″. *Fuller.* R.2/73.
Sword with an iron blade and a wooden handle. *"Benin.* Short wide bladed sword the handle not being of true Benin type. From a small collection of old Benin weapons and execution swords. 16 March 1948" (Fuller).

330. SWORD. *Iron.* L. 19½″. *Fuller.* R.2/71.
Sword with an iron blade and a wooden handle covered with brass wire fashioned into rope patterns. The hilt is studded with copper nails. *"Benin.* Short sword of the cleaver type. The 'chain' inlay on the handle is ingenious and consists of tiny staples driven into the wood through one another and bent over, the evenness with which it is done is remarkable. From a small collection of old Benin weapons and execution swords. For somewhat similar specimens see—Roth 'Great Benin,' p. 129, fig. 141, and Pitt-Rivers, p. 74, pl. 37, figs 84–85. 16 March, 1948" (Fuller).

331. SWORD. *Iron.* L. 22½″. *Fuller.* R.2/72.
Sword with an iron blade and a wooden handle decorated with copper rivets. *"Benin.* Short sword, very old specimen of Benin type. From a small collection of old Benin weapons and execution swords (see Pitt-Rivers, p. 96, Pl. 48, figs. 376–7 for a somewhat similar specimen). 16 March, 1948" (Fuller).

332. SWORD. *Iron.* L. 31″. *Fuller.* R.1/49. Sword with an iron blade and handle of cast bronze. *"Benin.* Sword with rattle handle. See Pitt-Rivers, p. 96, fig. 377. Also Oldman's Cat. 29, August 1905, No. 3 for this specimen. 1905" (Fuller).

333. SWORD and SCABBARD. *Iron, Leather, Wool.* L. Sword 22½″, L. Scabbard 22¼″. *Fuller.* R.1/56.

Sword with an iron blade and a wooden handle with strips of brass around it. On one side of the blade is an incised *ebē* and an animal. The sword is in a leather scabbard which is decorated with appliquéd red, green, yellow, and black felt stitched to a maroon plush material covering one side of the scabbard. The material is cut to form designs of birds, a horseman, and a lizard. In addition, linear designs of an *ebē*, guilloche, and others are formed by a very thin silver-colored wire stitched to the plush. The harness is of twined purple, green, red, and yellow yarn (wool?). The sword is similar in shape to that carried by the figure in 102 (Plate XLV). The scabbard seems rather large for the sword. *"Benin.* From a collection of old weapons brought from Benin. Short sword in elaborate scabbard. For a similar specimen of sword and scabbard, but not so fine, see Pitt-Rivers, p. 58, No. 213. An Ebere chiselled on blade. 16 March 1948" (Fuller).

334. DAGGER and SHEATH. *Iron, Leather.* L. of dagger 10½″, L. w. sheath 13¾″. *Fuller.* R.2/79.
Dagger with an iron blade and a wooden handle covered with leather and bound with three bands, two of brass and one of iron. There is a loop for a belt on the leather sheath. *"Benin.* Knife collected and brought back from Benin by Dr. F. Norman-Roth, the Medical Officer to the Expedition of 1897. Acquired by me from his widow, Mrs. Winifred Norman-Roth. 17 May, 1923" (Fuller).

335. SPEAR. *Wood* and *Iron.* L. 61¼″. *Fuller.* R.1/37.
A spear with a wooden shaft and an iron-barbed point of the shape of a laurel leaf. The butt is in the shape of a fluted knob. The socket of the iron point is hafted to the wooden shaft by being beaten round it. *"Benin.* A spear of very rare type and old. From the collection of Ralph Locke one of the two white survivors of the Massacre on the 4 Jan. 1897. 4 March 1930" (Fuller).

336. SPEAR. *Iron.* L. 66½″. *Fuller.* R.1/39.
"Benin. Spear entirely of iron in one piece. See Oldman's Cat. No. 29, August 1905, item 4, and Pitt-Rivers, p. 36, fig. 104. This specimen was brought from Benin. 1905" (Fuller).

337. STICK. *Wood* and *Iron.* L. 43½″. *Fuller.* R.1/40.
A carved wooden shaft with an iron point. At the top is a figure with a hand under his chin; in the middle is another figure holding on to his hat. The end of the stick is carved in the form of the head of a crocodile with, in its jaws, the end piece around which the socket of the iron point is bent. The crocodile motif recalls 151 (Plate XLVII), where the crocodile is shown with a mud fish in its mouth. Cf. 371. *"Benin.* A staff of unusual type. From the collection of Ralph Locke one of the two survivors of the Massacre on the 4 Jan. 1897. 4 March, 1930" (Fuller).

338. SPEARHEAD. *Iron.* L. 21″. *Fuller.* R.1/57.
A large iron spearhead with two large barbs, 3¼″ long, and, in very low relief, a snake form. *"Benin.* Iron spear head of old make with incised decoration. An almost exactly similar specimen is in the Pitt-Rivers collection except that it is of copper. (See 'Antique Works of Art from Benin' by General Pitt-Rivers p. 96, pl. 48, fig. 379.) 1 May, 1928" (Fuller).

339. SPEARHEAD. *Bronze.* L. 23⅞″. *Fuller.* R.1/58.
Spearhead of bronze with large barbs and chased designs. *"Benin.* A rare bronze spearhead, the blade being tooled with a crocodile, etc. (See Pitt-Rivers, p. 96, Pl. 48, figs. 177–9 for a somewhat similar specimen of copper but too soft a metal to be of much use.) This one would be quite useful. 16 March, 1948" (Fuller).

340. "SHRAPNEL" CHARGE. *Bamboo* and *Iron.* L. 11⅜″. *Fuller.* R.3/21.
A charge of shrapnel made of a number of bamboo splints, wrapped at five points

along their lengths with rattan, to form a cylinder containing jagged lumps of iron. "*West Africa. Benin River.* Charge of shot fired from a cannon obtained from the Portuguese. Collection of Ralph F. Locke, 1897. Dec. 1927. Such as this was fired from cannon obtained from Portuguese. The cannon were trained on creeks, and did much damage to occupants of a Naval Pinnace in 1894 at commencement of the trouble with Nana of Broheinne, a Jekri chief living in the swamp of Benin River. The contents are chiefly bits of broken 'imported' pots" (Fuller).

341. "Shrapnel" Charge. *Bamboo* and *Iron.* L. 11⅜". *Fuller.* R.3/22.
As 340.

342. Powder Flask. *Brass.* Ht. 13⅜". *CNHM* 91271.
Powder flask of cast brass with a long brass chain of thirty-eight links running from two eyelets approximately halfway down the body on each side. Near the top of the spout of the vessel are two further eyelets standing out from the body; from each, two links of chain keep the long chain close to the body of the flask.

Defensive Arms

343. Shield. *Wood.* L. 30". *Fuller.* R.1/50.
*
Shield of plaited strips of wood, rectangular in shap but with rounded corners, reinforced down the central ridge with sticks kept in place by strips inserted under the vertically plaited elements. The edges are reinforced with close stitches of some sort of split cane. The top of the shield is marked by a protrusion of the central ridge. On the back at the center is a handle formed of coiled withe.

344. Shield. *Wood.* L. 29½". *Fuller.* R.1/51.
Similar to 343.

345. Shield. *Wood.* L. 25¼". *Fuller.* R.1/52.
Oval-shaped shield, formed of strips of plaited wood much wider than those used for 343–45, with reinforcing sticks down the central ridge, which protrudes upward. The edges are finely stitched with some sort of split rattan. Inside is a plaited handle.

346. Shield. *Wood.* Max. Diam. 25". *Fuller.* R.1/53.
Shield similar to 345 but round and lacking a handle and the protruding central ridge. "*Benin* or *Locality.* These type of shields are called Benin and I have an old specimen which was brought from that city, but I think they were in use over a much larger area. This one is old and unusual, being circular. 5 October 1932" (Fuller).

347. Shield. *Wood.* L. 25". W. 17¾". *CNHM* 89688.
*
Oval-shaped shield of very wide plaited strips of bark-covered wood. The edge is closely stitched with split cane. The central ridge protrudes.

VARIOUS

Recent Brass Casting

When Dr. W. D. Hambly visited Nigeria on the F. H. Rawson–Field Museum Ethnological Expedition to West Africa, he collected a few objects which represented certain stages in the lost wax process of casting as well as examples of modern work which was being undertaken by the traditional brass-workers at the Benin Divisional Council's crafts school with the encouragement of the Oba. These objects and examples are given below (348–56).

348. SPOON. *Wax.* L. 7⅞″. W. 1½″. CNHM 209417.

"Wax model for casting a brass spoon (see 352 for finished brass spoon). The wax model is enclosed in a clay mold which is baked—wax runs out—molten brass poured in to fill space left by wax" (Hambly).

349. INVESTMENT. *Clay.* L. 8⅝″. W. 2¾″. CNHM 209458.

"A mold of red clay used by the brass smelter. This contains a wax spoon—when the mold is heated the wax runs out, so leaving space for molten brass. Finally the clay is broken away and the brass spoon is filed smooth" (Hambly).

350. CRUCIBLE. *Clay.* L. 4¼″. W. 3½″. CNHM 209457.

"A mold of clay used for melting brass. This has not been used and is therefore unburnt except for the necessary hardening" (Hambly).

351. CRUCIBLE. *Clay.* L. 4″. W. 3½″. CNHM 209456.

"Clay mold used for smelting brass—this has been used in the furnace" (Hambly).

352. SPOON. *Brass.* L. 7½″. W. 1⅝″. CNHM 209416.

"Brass spoon made by cire perdue process. This is the final stage—spoon has been removed from clay mold in which it was cast and the final filing has been given" (Hambly).

353. BELL. *Brass.* Ht. 5½″. W. 2¾″. CNHM 209562.
*

Cast brass bell ornamented with scalloped designs. Spaces between filled with punch marks.

354. MUG. *Brass.* Ht. 4¼″. L. 2¾″. CNHM 209560.
*

"Brass drinking vessel made by *cire-perdue* process" (Hambly). Rosette border near top.

355. JUG. *Brass.* Ht. 4¼″. L. 2⅜″. CNHM 209561.
*

"Cast brass jug ornamented by punching after jug was made" (Hambly).

356. CANDLESTICK. *Brass.* Ht. 7⅛″. L. 2″. CNHM 209559.
*

"Cast brass candlestick of native work but in imitation of European forms" (Hambly).

Miscellaneous Objects

357. BOX. *Coconut.* L. 4½″. W. 3½″. Fuller. R.3/14.

Decorated with low-relief carving. On the cover are two figures in European dress holding a snake between them. On the other half are shown two figures holding a third, perhaps a king, between them.

358. BOTTLE. *Coconut.* L. 3¾″. Fuller. R.3/13.

Decorated with low-relief designs of a scaly fish, three small snakes, and a mud fish. Coconuts were carved by the *amada*, the king's male servants. (Cf. Pitt-Rivers, 1900: Pl. 30, Figs. 217–18).

359. BOTTLE. *Coconut.* L. 4½″. Fuller. R.3/15.

Decorated with low-relief guilloche design.

360. JUG. *Bronze.* Ht. 9¾″. W. 4¾″. (at top). CNHM 91262.

Round the top of the vessel, in high relief, are two snails and two tortoises. The lid is missing. There are more elaborate and finer examples in the Lagos and Berlin museums.

361. VESSEL. *Bronze.* Ht. 3¾″. Max. Diam. 3″. Fuller. R.2/32.

This strange object, conical in shape, does not function as a vessel in that it will not stand upright on its curved base (a cap for the end of a tusk?). Its surface is decorated in low relief with guilloche designs and a snake, whose head bites the right leg of a man. The man holds in his right hand a horn or dagger. In his left hand he holds a bag. A snake curves round the flanged top of the vessel and bites its own tail.

362. WINE GLASS. *Bronze.* Ht. 4″. Max. Diam. 2⅛″. *Fuller.* R.2/29.

The stem is formed of a male figure with arms upraised, supporting the lower sides of the vessel. "*Benin.* From the collection of Ralph Locke, one of the two survivors of the Massacre of Jan. 4, 1897. 4 March 1930" (Fuller).

363. LADLE. *Ivory.* L. 15″. *Fuller.* R.2/67.

The handle ends in a clenched hand, similar to certain rattle staffs. "*Benin.* 26/6/30. Collection Rev. E. E. Hill of West Malling" (Fuller).

364. MANILLA. *Brass.* Max Diam. 2⅜″. *Fuller.* C.

Used widely as a form of currency on the coast. (Loan Book, p. 63, No. 50. "26/6/30" (Fuller).

365. MANILLA. *Brass.* Max. Diam. 2⅜″. *Fuller.* D.

"Loan Book p. 63. No. 50." "26/6/30."

366. NAIL. *Iron and Brass.* L. 6¾″. *Fuller.* R.3/25.

An iron nail surmounted by a small brass figure cast on the nail. "*Benin.* Iron & Bronze object—said to be a crucifixion nail, but may be a tool or chisel for engraving. 11 February 1913" (Fuller).

367. NAIL. *Iron* and *Lead*(?). L. 5¾″. *CNHM* 89818.

Similar to 366. Figure of lead with eyelet on back.

368. ORNAMENT. *Brass* (Beaten). W. 13¾″. *CNHM* 89804.

Plate XLIII

The top part of an ornament worn down the back by certain chiefs (see Talbot, 1926: Fig. 138, opposite p. 546). It is made of beaten brass parts riveted together, the central theme representing a crocodile. The whole ornament included a long beaten-brass tail, 2–3 feet long, attached to this circular top part (cf. Pitt-Rivers, 1900: Pl. 40, Fig. 306).

369. PIPE. *Brass* and *Wood.* L. 11⅞″. *Fuller.* R.2/68.

Bowl of cast brass, stem of wood. "?Be-nin. For a very similar pipe from Benin see Webster's *Catalogue,* Vol. III, No. 21, p. 7" (Fuller).

370. SOCKET. *Bronze.* L. 1¾″. W. 2″. *CNHM* 91265.

Socket or mount of cast bronze with, in relief, two chameleons, one on either side of a leopard.

371. STAFF. *Wood.* L. 60½″. *Fuller.* R.1/28.

At the top of this carved staff is a Janus head; below is the handle with, below again, two low-relief heads similar in style to the two heads flanking the European smoking a pipe on stool 304 and on an end piece of stool 303 (Plate XIV). Between the two heads, on each side is a fish in low relief. Beaten-brass strips and copper nails are used for decorative purposes (cf. Gwato style). "Sacrificial mace still bearing the effects of the human sacrifices. 28.1.32" (Fuller).

372. TONGS. *Iron.* L. 11¾″. *CNHM* 89816.

Blacksmith's tongs.

373. WHIP. *Leather, Wood,* and *Bronze.* L. 33⅛″. *Fuller.* R.2/75.

"*Benin.* A whip of 10 tails the handle decorated with 5 spiral rings of copper or bronze over hide surrounding a wooden core. Horse whips are not common in Benin city and that animal was little used there for riding and this specimen may be of Hausa provenience, but it comes from a small collection of old Benin weapons. Such whips my be the prototype of the coral and other fly-whisks used ceremonially in Benin and elsewhere in Nigeria. 16 March, 1948" (Fuller).

STYLES OF THE BENIN REGION

This section includes objects which may or may not have been made at Benin or in the region of Benin and objects which have often been thought to be Benin workmanship but which can now be identified as coming from a different provenience.

Reference was made under "Weapons" to a short sword, 333, which was brought back from Benin but which, though having present certain Benin designs, would seem to be of Yoruba origin. Reference was also made under "Shield Plaques" to an Ife-Benin style and to a Huntsman style. The CNHM collection contains several pyramidal-shaped bells which have a curved bottom edge rather than a straight one and which are lighter in weight than Benin examples. In style they appear similar. Bells 374 and 375 have the Huntsman marking mentioned, whereas 376 and 377 do not. Chief Ine of the brassworkers identified these bells as coming from Uhen, a village on the Edo-Yoruba border.

374. BELL. *Brass.* Ht. 7⅞″. W. 3¾″. *CNHM* 89749.
Pyramidal in shape with upcurving edges. On the front panel are rudimentary nose and eyes. Huntsman markings. Iron clapper.

375. BELL. *Brass.* Ht. 6 5/16″. W. 3 15/16″. *CNHM* 89750.
Similar to 374 except that the mouth and part of the forehead, which is striated, are also indicated.

376. BELL. *Brass.* Ht. 4⅜″. W. 2¾″. *CNHM* 89748.
Somewhat similar to 374 but lacking Huntsman marks and having straight rather than upcurving edges. Greenish patina.

377. BELL. *Brass.* Ht. 7½″. W. 4¾″. *CNHM* 91257.
Similar to 376 and also lacking Huntsman marks.

378. BELL. *Brass.* Ht. 4⅜″. Diam. 2¾″. *CNHM* 89752.
Globular with similar nose and eyes to 374.

379. BELL. *Brass.* Ht. 3½″. Diam. 2″. *CNHM* 89753.
Globular with greenish patina in places. Igbo work(?).

In 1900 Lieutenant General Pitt-Rivers included in the publication of his collection of Benin antiquities several objects which are of Jekri origin. In the Fuller Collection the following four objects are Jekri work.

380. COMB. *Wood.* L. 16⅞″. *Fuller.* A. "Probably *Jekri.* The chain carving suggests this" (Fuller). Acquired 13/1/1947.

381. PADDLE. Wood. L. 57¼″. Max. W. 5⅞″. *Fuller.* R.1/34.
"*West. Africa.* Benin territory or coast. This does not resemble the usual Jekri modern (trade?) paddle (see Pitt-Rivers 'Antique Works of Art from Benin,' pl. 33, figs. 256–7) but is a business implement of considerable age and most unusual carving. It strongly resembles Benin City workmanship in detail and design." (Fuller).

382. PADDLE. *Wood.* L. 65½″. Max. W. 5⅞″. *Fuller.* R.1/35.
"*Benin District.* An old Jekri paddle. An unusually fine specimen. From the collection of Ralph Locke one of the two survivors of the Massacre on the 4th Jan. 1897. 4 March 1930" (Fuller).

383. PADDLE. *Wood.* L. 65½″. Max W. 5⅞″. *Fuller.* R.1/36.
"*Benin District.* A Jekri paddle of some age and a good specimen. From the collection of Ralph Locke one of the two white survivors of the 4th Jan. 1897. 4 March 1930" (Fuller).

A number of ivory objects have often thought to be Benin workmanship but either are the work of the Yoruba at Owo or appertain to a grouping referred to in the introductory text and designated by William Fagg as "Afro-Portuguese" (Fagg and Forman, W. and B., 1959). Objects of

Owo origin are known in Benin. Dr. Bradbury sent me a photograph some years ago which showed a number of ivory carvings of Owo style belonging to an Edo man. A clear distinction between Owo and Benin work is apparently not always made by the modern Edo.

384. RATTLE. *Ivory.* L. 17". *Fuller.* B.
A fine ivory carving, following the form of a tusk, of a rattle with an ivory clapper and the form of a kneeling female figure holding a fan in front of her genitals. Above her is a bird (an ibis?). Owo work.

385. CUP. *Ivory.* Ht. 3¾". *Fuller.* R.2/28.
An ivory cup with a lid on the top of which is an animal (leopard?). Afro-Portuguese in style. "*Benin.* Resembles 16th century Benin work. 19 July 1938" (Fuller).

Further Items

386. SKULL OF A LEOPARD. *Bronze.* L. 7". *Fuller.* R.0/64.
Several bronze skulls of leopards are in museum collections (notably, Stockholm); they appear to be Benin work. The leopard skull also appears on one or two plaques (e.g., British Museum 98.1–15.175. Illustrated in Read & Dalton, 1899: xxxii/2). This particular skull, which has one incisor missing, would appear, however, to be Igbo work. "*Benin.* A leopard's skull much stylized. The back portion fashioned to resemble the front possibly for symmetry. From the collection of Dr. Allman, CMG, the Principal Medical Officer to the Punitive Expedition 1897. 23 Sept. 1937" (Fuller).

387. SPEAR. *Wood* and *Iron.* L. 72". *Fuller.* R.1/38.
Spear with long carved haft and an iron spearhead, the socket of which has been bent round the haft and secured with a nail through the iron socket and wooden haft. "*Benin.* A rare spear with carved haft. From the collection of Ralph Locke one of the two white survivors of the Massacre of 4 Jan. 1897. 4 March 1937" (Fuller).

388. STAFF. *Wood.* L. 39". *CNHM* 89689.
Staff of four carved nude figures, one kneeling female above an oblong of relief designs, consisting of two leopards above a snake with, below, two male figures in full relief and, below them, a second female figure, squatting. The style of this carving calls to mind carvings seen at Oja in Kukuruku, an area which is on the edges of the old Benin Kingdom.

389. FONT or MORTAR. *Stone.* Ht. 5". Max. Diam. 8⅜". *Fuller.* R.2/25.
This object was referred to by Captain Fuller as a font. It has six fins.

390. BEATER. *Ivory.* L. 11". *CNHM* 89715.
*
Small round handle, crosshatched decoration at top, with a larger body than handle. Said to be a bark-cloth beater. (*Edo* work?)

391. RAM'S HEAD. *Wood.* Ht. 15". W. 10". *CNHM* 91260.
This finely carved head of a ram comes from Owo, an eastern city of the Yoruba. The head of a ram is a form which also occurs in Benin art in several contexts; a fine ram in the round, cast of bronze, is in the British Museum. Captain Landolphe visited Benin in 1778 and a number of times subsequently. In his memoirs he recalls observations on the burial of a chief and refers to carved wooden heads of rams as supports for tusks "well carved with images of lizards and snakes" being placed on the altar of the deceased (see Roth, 1903: 42). Carved rams' heads are still to be seen on certain ancestor shrines in the Benin region today but are not known to exist in Benin. In Benin, wooden heads, such as 129 (Plate XXXIX), are placed on ancestor shrines to deceased chiefs, as referred to under "heads." Illustrated in Webster's *Catalogue*, V, 106, Fig. 172.

PLATES

PLATE XLVIII

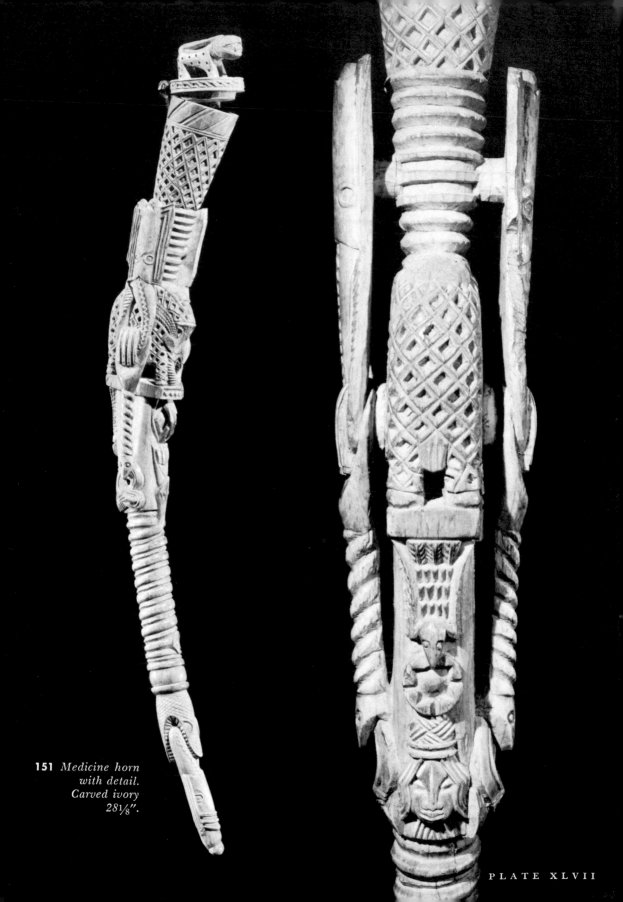

151 *Medicine horn
with detail.
Carved ivory
28⅛″.*

PLATE XLVII

PLATE XLVI

102 *Figure of a warrior chief. Bronze. 15⅛".*

PLATE XLV

45 *Kola-nut box depicting two memorial heads. Wood, beaten brass, inlaid coconut shell. 22″.*

268 *Plaque showing a snake with a fish in its mouth. Bronze. 16″.*

PLATE XLIV

7, 9, 10 *Three armlets. Bronze. Left to right, 5½", 5⅜", and 5¾".*

368 *Part of back ornament worn by a chief. Beaten brass. 13¾".*

PLATE XLIII

PLATE XLII

260 *Plaque depicting a warrior chief. Bronze. 15⅜″.*

PLATE XLI

307 *Carved tusk with detail showing warrior with a spear in each hand. Ivory. 5′6″.*

PLATE XL

PLATE XXXIX

249 *Plaque depicting European. Bronze. 15⅝″.*

PLATE XXXVIII

161 *Bell with depictions of Europeans. Bronze. 7".*

PLATE XXXVII

191, 190 *Two bells. Bronze.* 5¾″ *and* 5⅜″.

53 *Bracelet with depictions of horses' heads. Bronze. Diam.,* 4⅞″.

PLATE XXXVI

124 *Head in memory of a king. Bronze. 20½″.*

PLATE XXXV

143, 142 *Two lamps. Brass. Left, 23¼″; right, 16½″.*

271 *Plaque showing fish with a little fish in its mouth. Bronze. 14½″.*

PLATE XXXIV

254 *Plaque with detail showing chief dressed as a warrior. Bronze.* 16¾″.

PLATE XXXIII

PLATE
XXXII

PLATE XXXI

284, 286, 285 *Three fragments of pendant plaques. Bronze. Left to right, 5¾", 4¾", and 5½".*

288, 287 *Two pendant plaques, depicting women. Bronze. Left, 5⅜"; right, 4¾".*

PLATE XXX

308 *Carved tusk and detail showing warrior with shield and spear. Ivory. 4'.*

PLATE XXIX

118 *Head in memory of a king. Bronze. 8⅛″. (Collection City Art Museum of St. Louis.)*

PLATE XXVIII

PLATE XXVII

247 *Two sides of plaque depicting two Europeans. Bronze. 16¾".*

PLATE XXVI

130 *Head in memory of a queen-mother. Bronze, iron. 16¾".*

PLATE XXV

103 *Figure of a king. Bronze. 26¾″.*

135, 134, 133 *Three keys. Bronze.*
Left: top, 5⅝″, bottom, 5⅛″;
right, 7⅜″.

PLATE XXIV

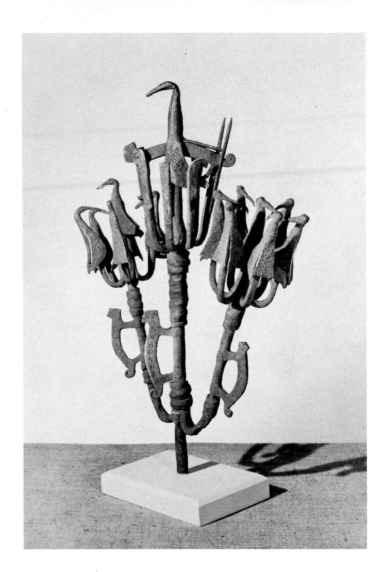

152 *Medicine staff. Iron. 26⅜".*

48 *Kola-nut box. Wood, ornamented with bands of beaten brass. Diam., 15¾".*

PLATE XXIII

239 *Ornamental mask with profile. Bronze. 7¾".*

PLATE XXII

300, 299 *Two plaques depicting leopards' heads. Beaten brass. Left, 7½"; right, 7½".*

PLATE XXI

95, 98, 97, 96 *Four figures from stands. Bronze. Left to right,* 4¾″, 8⅛″, 7⅞″, *and* 5½″.

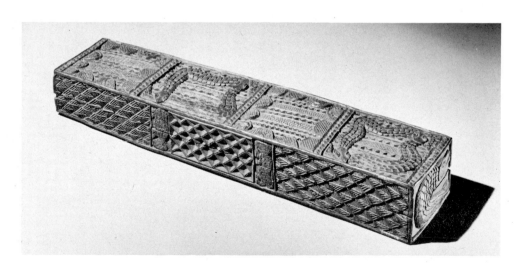

47 *Kola-nut box. Wood. L.,* 19¾″.

PLATE XX

101 *Figure shown wearing bead shirt and winged cap. Bronze, cast on rod. 10½".*

PLATE XIX

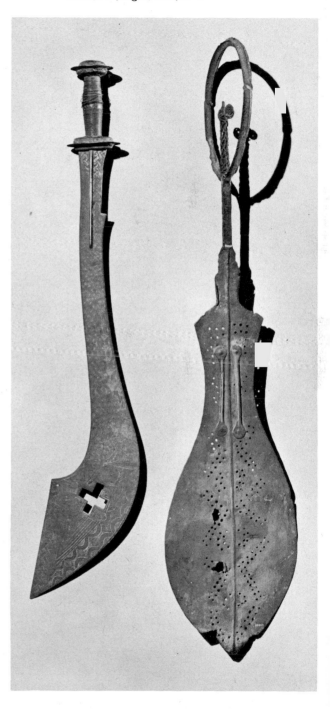

325, 318 *Two ceremonial swords. Left, cast brass, 34"; right, iron, 38".*

140 *Yam knife, with handle terminating in Janus memorial head. Iron, brass. 7½".*

PLATE XVIII

306 *Carved tusk, with detail showing European. Ivory. 7'4".*

PLATE XVII

283 *Pendant plaque, depicting European on horseback. Bronze. 6¾".*

PLATE XVI

266 *Plaque showing man playing a gong. Bronze. 20¼"*

PLATE XV

303 *Carved stool with details. Wood. Ht., 13⅞″.*

Detail of carved rosette on other side of stool showing woman carrying a tray. At her left is an altar with two rattles and a memorial head and tusk. Diam., 5½″.

Detail of top of stool, depicting a European with two Edo on either side, all armed. L., 25″.

PLATE XIV

126 *Head in Udo style. Bronze. 8⅝″.*

272 *Plaque depicting two mud fish. Bronze. 12⅛″.*

PLATE XIII

105 *Two views of a figure of a king seated on a throne. Ivory. 15½".*

PLATE XII

221, 217, 214, 216, 215 *Five rattles. Carved wood, the one on the left covered with cowrie shells. Left to right: 46″, 47⅝″, 52⅜″, 56½″, and 49⅜″.*

217, 214, 215 *Details of three rattles. Wood.*

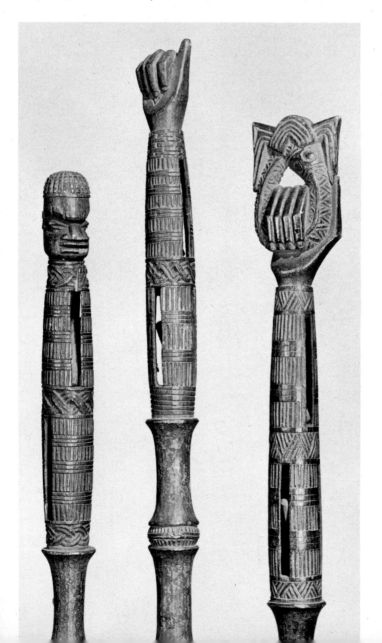

PLATE XI

76 *Cock. Bronze. 20″.*

PLATE X

PLATE IX

122 *Two views of a head in memory of a king. Note leopard on base flange. Bronze. 12⅝".*

PLATE VIII

274 *Plaque representing the head of a crocodile. Bronze. 18¾".*

267 *Plaque depicting a snake with rare background of a circle with a cross in it. Bronze. 11½".*

PLATE VII

117 *Head, early. Bronze.* 7¾".

PLATE VI

204, 205 *Two ibis-effigy idiophones. Bronze. Left, 13¼"; right, 13¾".*

PLATE V

PLATE IV

PLATE III

93, 92 *Front and rear views of two fans. Hide, wood, flannel. Left, 21¼″; right, 21⅞″.*

PLATE II

250 *Plaque depicting three kings. Bronze. 15⅝″.*

PLATE I